Year
of the Big Snow

By the Same Author

FIRST THROUGH THE GRAND CANYON:
THE EXPEDITION OF MAJOR JOHN WESLEY POWELL

YEAR
OF THE BIG SNOW

John Charles Frémont's Fourth Expedition

Steve Frazee

Holt, Rinehart and Winston
New York / Chicago / San Francisco

TO LINDA

Author's Foreword

IN 1848 THE OLD Missouri Lion, U.S. Senator Thomas Hart Benton, was roaring for a Pacific railroad by a central route from St. Louis to San Francisco. He spoke of travelers "flying" on fast trains across the Rocky Mountains. Carved in the granite of a peak above them would stand a statue of Columbus, with outstretched arm pointing westward.

Senator Benton's son-in-law was John Charles Frémont, the Great Pathmarker. At thirty-five, Frémont was famous because of three successful expeditions through the West.

Starting in 1842, Frémont, then an Army lieutenant, had led mapping parties across the Rockies on his first expedition. On his second expedition he charted the Oregon Trail, went south to California, and returned across the deserts and plains without serious difficulties.

In 1845, Frémont set forth on his third expedition.

The Washington *Daily Union* said that he was "determined upon a complete military and scientific exploration of all the vast unknown region between the Rocky Mountains and the Pacific Ocean, and between the Oregon River and the Gulf of California."

The United States was about to acquire California, then a Mexican possession. Frémont's third expedition was actually more military than scientific. He arrived in California in time for the Bear Flag Revolution, a revolt of American settlers against the Mexican government.

There was confusion in Washington. The War Department instructed the Army to seize and govern California, while the Navy Department issued the same orders to its commanders. Frémont, who had just been promoted to lieutenant colonel, was caught in the conflict between high ranking officers of the Army and Navy.

He obeyed what seemed to him to be the authorized command, the Navy. As a result he was sent back to Washington in disgrace to face a court-martial for insubordination. The trial lasted for three months during the winter of 1847-48.

The verdict was dismissal from the Army. President James Polk approved the verdict, but remitted the sentence and ordered Frémont back to duty.

But considering himself unfairly charged and unfairly tried, Frémont resigned from the Army.

Though he would no longer have government backing for an expedition, Frémont was eager to start a fourth expedition, and Senator Benton was just as eager to have him find that central route for a transcontinental railroad.

The court-martial had been a bitter blow. Both Frémont and Senator Benton thought that a successful expedition would erase the effects of the Army trial and carry Frémont to new heights as a public figure.

No man of the time was better qualified to head such an exploration. Frémont was bold, dashing, hardy—and lucky. He was a good commander of men. He was also imaginative. On one of his earlier expeditions he had used the first rubber raft ever tried out by an American explorer, and in 1843 he had tried to use photography as an aid to mapping.

Frémont and Benton agreed that the central route should follow the 38th parallel as closely as possible. The 38th parallel drawn on a map did lead just where they wished the railroad to go.

In what is now Colorado, the parallel crosses the Rocky Mountains, which are not just a simple line of peaks dividing East and West. They are gigantic ranges of mountains running in many directions, crashing into each other wildly. To pass among them a man must know what he is doing.

Frémont, who would still be called colonel, did not plan to cast about blindly, seeking a pass. He would hire a Mountain Man to guide him, one of the old trappers who had spent many years exploring the Rockies in search of beaver. Kit Carson and other Mountain Men had guided Frémont before.

The fourth expedition was privately financed, well supplied, splendidly equipped. Everything would move by pack train of about 130 mules. The success of the journey, and life itself, would depend upon the mules.

Of the thirty-five men who started, twenty-two were veterans of Western travel. Many of them had been with Frémont on previous expeditions.

Foremost among the veterans was lighthearted Alexis Godey, of French stock from St. Louis, who ranked with Kit Carson himself. He took along his nephew, Theodore McNabb, who was fourteen years old.

On October 20, 1848, the expedition struck out from Westport, now part of Kansas City, Missouri. Frémont expected to be in California about January 8, 1849.

They made good time until they reached the snowy mountains.

The story of what happened to the fourth expedition of John Charles Frémont is taken from the journals of the men who were there, from their letters, and from the mute evidence of campsites in the high country of Colorado.

—S. F.

Contents

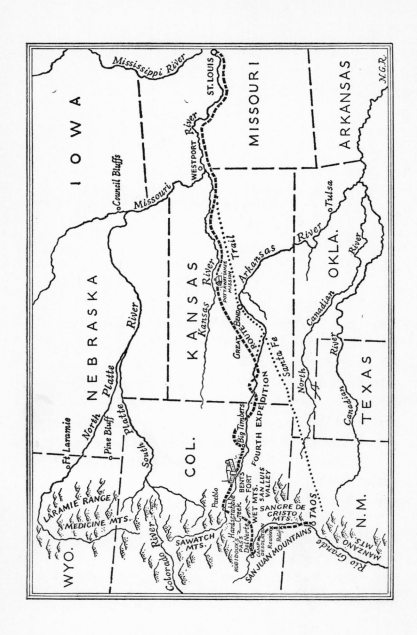

CHAPTER 1

Expedition Snow

THAT DAY WHEN THE expedition first saw buffalo on the fringe of the Smoky Hills, Ted McNabb's heart jumped in his chest. He wanted to drop everything and charge out after the huge brown beasts. Though he was only fourteen, he was big and strong for his age. He figured he could ride and shoot well enough to make quite a showing once he got out among the buffalo, churning dust a half-mile away.

He rode up along the pack train of tall, quick-stepping mules to where his uncle had stopped his horse to watch the buffalo. "Uncle Alexis . . ."

"I know, I know," Alexis Godey said, waving one hand. "You want to ride like a Comanche out there and kill animals right and left."

"Yes!" Ted licked dust from his lips, his eyes still on the running buffalo. At first they had appeared slow and lumbering, but he could see that they had covered a lot of ground in a short time. "Why not?"

"Why not, he asks me!" Godey rolled his eyes at the sky. He was a lithe, handsome man, with long, dark, curling hair. "You are riding a mule."

"I can make it run."

"No doubt, but where?" Godey's flashing smile took most of the sting out of his refusal. "Right now see about that slipping pack over there." Godey rode away.

After a few moments, Ted realized that no pack was slipping. In fact, the mules in his charge were way up the line. He hurried his mount, Ney, to overtake them.

Maybe the sight of a few buffalo was of no great importance, but Ted noticed that almost everyone in the cavalcade was excited.

Off to the left, he saw three riders on a hill. He recognized Captain Andrew Cathcart's horse, and guessed that the two men with him were John Scott and Tom Martin, hunters for the expedition.

Cathcart shouted and went after the buffalo, with Scott and Martin close behind him. Ted watched them enviously. Cathcart was a magnificent rider, an officer of the British II Hussars. He was a medium-sized man, erect and usually trim, with a short sandy beard. He had come along on the expedition as a sportsman in search of adventure. Soon he was far out in front of his two companions. The buffalo had broken into small groups and were running hard—tiny, dark blots against the long hills.

Godey was riding at the head of the pack train now, with Colonel Frémont and two of the Delaware scouts.

Ted could see his uncle gesturing with both hands, as he talked to Frémont.

It was Sunday, October 29, 1848, a cloudy day with a cold wind riffling the dead brown grass. This was the fourth expedition of John Charles Frémont, nine days out from Westport, Missouri. It was on the way to California to find a route for a railroad that would someday run clear across America.

Ted McNabb didn't doubt in the least that Colonel Frémont would do just as he planned. He was a man to admire, though when Ted had met him for the first time in St. Louis, Frémont had seemed something less than he had expected.

Ted didn't know just what he thought a great explorer should look like, but, at first impression, Frémont didn't fill the bill. He was a restless, slightly built man, with a sad look in his dark eyes that reminded Ted of pictures of poets he had seen.

"So this is the young man you've been telling me about," Colonel Frémont said to Godey. He shook Ted's hand. "I must say, McNabb, if you're at all like your uncle, you'll be a great asset to my expedition."

"I hope so, sir." Ted felt pretty good about being called simply by his last name, instead of Master McNabb.

Now, out on the Smoky Hill Trail, Colonel Frémont was no longer the well-dressed gentleman, and Godey was not an elegant dandy. Dust, hard riding, and campfire soot had changed the appearance of everyone.

One mule, Poche, started to break from the mule train. Ted bore in against him with Ney. Poche snaked his long neck around and snapped at Ney, and then fell back in line.

Ted watched the place where the hunters had disappeared. He listened for the sound of shooting, but he guessed he couldn't have heard it anyway, above the scrape and clatter of the shod mules and the creaking of heavy packs.

Antoine Morin rode up beside Ted. He was a grizzled Frenchman, one of the oldest, most respected men of the expedition. In his travels with Frémont and others, he had seen many places in the West not yet on maps. On the second day of the trip he had been kicked in the face by a mule, and his mouth was still badly swollen.

"How's the cut lip today?" Ted asked.

Old Antoine shrugged. "It is nothing. One becomes careless, and there is always something waiting to bite him." He gestured toward the vanished hunters. "You would like to be with them, yes?"

Ted nodded.

"There is time."

"Yeah, that's what Godey said."

Antoine tried to smile. "Do every day the things that must be done. Listen well. Watch. Learn." He glanced at Poche. "And do not let that one kick your head off." He winked and rode out to the side to get away from the dust.

About noon the pack train of 130 mules crossed the Smoky Hill Fork, a slow stream with muddy banks that caused the mules to slip and slide. After the cavalcade climbed up from the crossing, beside a bluff of green clay and sand, the land ahead flattened suddenly. The overcast was heavier, and the wind was growing colder.

Not long afterward, Ned Kern caught up with Ted and rode beside him. Ned was the artist of the expedition. He was twenty-five, a tall, dark-haired man.

"Godey's somewhere up ahead?" he asked.

"The last I saw."

"I think I'll go up and see if he wants to chase a bull or two," Ned said, grinning. He trotted on.

There were three Kerns in the expedition, all brothers. Ned was the youngest; Dick was a few years older; and then there was the doctor, Benjamin, a quiet man who wasn't too easy to know. Of all the members of the company, Ned Kern was one of those Ted liked best.

As the train pushed on in the face of the wind, the guns of the Indian hunters cracked in the river bottom. They were hunting ducks and turkeys and coons. Besides the Delawares, there were three California Indians with the expedition; Gregorio and Joaquin were Tulares. Manuel was a Cosumne. That was the life, being a hunter, Ted thought.

Ted glared at Poche and Scrap and the other two mules that he packed and unpacked every day.

"Stay in line, you!" he growled, though the animals were behaving themselves.

Scott and Martin came in from their hunt with chunks of meat tied to their saddles. Ted joined the others crowding around the hunters.

"Bool?" Antoine said. "You bring meat from old buffalo bools? Better we boil our boots."

"Bulls was all we could find," Martin said.

Haler came riding back to see what was going on. His real name was Lorenzo Vincenthaler, though everyone called him Haler, thinking that Vincent was a first name. "Where's the Englishman?" he asked.

"Cathcart? The last we saw of him, he was chasing some bulls lickety-split toward the river," Martin said.

"Didn't you look for him afterward?" Haler's way of asking questions always seemed to put blame on someone.

"Cathcart knows how to take care of himself," Martin said. "He'll be along."

Haler rode away to report to Colonel Frémont. He spent a lot of time carrying news to Frémont.

The long wind of the plains was bitter when the time approached for the cavalcade to camp. Colonel Frémont selected the campsite and sent Haler riding back to pass the word. As the shout, "Camp ahead!" went down the line, the mules moved a little more briskly.

Leaving the open, windswept plain, the train dropped into a wooded hollow near the river.

"Get 'em unloaded!" Godey shouted. He and Ned Kern had returned from their buffalo hunt—unsuccessful.

Setting up camp, like breaking camp, was always done as quickly as possible. The mules had to be unpacked at once, or else they would roll with their burdens, scattering equipment to the four winds. Then they had to be front-hobbled and turned out to graze.

After more than a week on the trail, the routine had fallen into shape fairly well, but there were always incidents. The same mule that had kicked Antoine in the face tried again, and missed.

Three times Poche tried to roll while Ted was loosening his pack. Each time Ted leaped quickly to shoulder against the mule and jerk his head around. Next Poche attempted a sly kick, a forward motion of his hind leg. Since he was shod, such a blow could inflict a painful injury or even break a leg.

Ted jumped out of the way. Then he kicked the mule, not hard enough to hurt him, but with force enough to let Poche know that his nonsense was not appreciated. After that the mule behaved, though he did jerk at Ted's heavy blanket coat with his teeth while being hobbled.

The company set up camp quickly, each man doing his part. On the hills the wind was still strong, but in the sheltered hollow the force of it was broken. Soon cooking fires were crackling.

It was then that Captain Cathcart came limping in, leading his horse. He had lost one boot and his clothes were plastered with blue mud.

"Where's the buffalo, Captain?" asked Charlie Taplin, one of Frémont's old hands.

Cathcart shook his head and grinned. "Tricky beasts. The bunch I was pursuing jumped down a steep bank into the river. It must have been a fifteen-foot drop."

"Why didn't you jump after them, Captain?" Ned Kern asked.

Cathcart gave him a surprised look. "I did." He said it so seriously that everyone laughed.

Cathcart turned his back to a fire, rubbing his thighs. "I jumped down the bank after them. My horse went end over end and so did I, pistol and powder flying into the river. My horse was down in the water, tangled up in some brush and trying to drown itself.

"While I was helping it up, my feet stuck in the mud and one boot pulled off. I never did find it."

Doc Kern asked, "You're not hurt?"

"Just my dignity," Cathcart answered.

For supper that night Ted roasted a piece of buffalo meat. Antoine and the California Indians were roasting a possum that dripped grease into the fire.

Though he ate his fill of the "old bool," Ted admitted to himself that maybe a boot would have tasted about as good or, as Antoine had said, even better.

That night, along with Micajah McGehee, Ted drew first guard duty on the mule herd. Even when hobbled, if the animals took a notion to go somewhere, they could travel miles during the night.

His first time on guard duty, Ted had fancied Indians crouching in every shadow. Once or twice he had almost fired his rifle. His uncle had bet him that at least once before they crossed the plains Ted would rouse the camp by shooting at nothing.

"I bet you I don't!" Ted had said.

"What is worse is *not* to give a warning, if Indians really are trying to steal the animals."

It made quite a problem. Ted didn't want to be laughed at for shooting at a bush, but neither did he want to stand like a bump on a pickle and let Indians stampede the mules. So far Ted had been lucky. Every shadow that made him suspicious when he was on guard had turned out to be harmless.

From the darkness of the trees he looked back on the camp. The best time of all was the two hours after dusk, when men gathered around a big fire to relax. It was then they told tales of their adventures: of trapping, Indian fights, and hunting grizzly bears.

Raphael Proue was talking now. He gestured with both hands. Firelight fell on the quiet faces of men listening to him. Proue had been with Frémont on all his expeditions. He had an endless store of exciting stories. But from where he was, Ted couldn't hear a word that was being said.

Near a smaller fire, Charles Preuss had set up his folding table and was working on a map. He was a stocky, red-faced German, with a crown of wild, curly hair. Frederick Creutzfeldt, the botanist, was with him. They paid no attention to what Proue was saying.

Godey had once said of Preuss that if Indians came roaring into camp unexpectedly, the map maker would ignore them, unless they disturbed his work.

Ted heard the mules moving restlessly as they foraged. He worked his way around the herd slowly, talking softly to the animals, until he came to McGehee.

McGehee was about twenty-two, a pleasant young Mississippian who had come along on the expedition for adventure. Now he was getting it—guarding mules. "Everything all right on this end?" Ted asked.

"All quiet—and cold." McGehee shivered. "I hope I get used to this cold before we hit the mountains. I've heard that there's places out there where it's winter the year around."

Ted tried to look westward through the night, to en-
vision the high reaching mountains that Godey had described to him. What did a few mountains amount to?
This expedition would cross them and go on to where
the Pacific broke against the warm land of California.

But before he got there, Ted vowed that he was going
to shoot a buffalo or two, even if he had to sneak away
from the pack train to do it.

CHAPTER 2

Buffalo Running

THE NEXT MORNING TWO hours before daylight one of the guards began to rouse the camp. This was the hardest time of all for Ted. Wrapped in his blankets in the linen tent that he shared with Godey and two others, he tried to catch a few more winks of sleep.

Then his uncle grabbed the blankets and rolled him out on the ground. "Up, up!" Godey said. "The sun is overhead."

Ted pulled on his boots and stumbled out of the tent. Some of the cooking fires were already going. Saunders Jackson, a free Negro who was Colonel Frémont's cook, was always one of the first men up. He had already made coffee.

He handed a cup of it to Frémont when the Colonel ducked out of his tent, his breath smoking in the frosty air. Frémont glanced at the still overcast sky. He scratched his

11

short, dark beard as he leaned over to peer at a thermometer fixed to a stake.

Frémont might have been up half the night, writing or poring over maps with Preuss, but he always looked fresh and full of energy in the morning.

Still yawning, Ted went down to the river to wash some of the sleep out of his eyes.

There was no loitering in the morning. Breakfast was gobbled hastily. Some of the old-timers like Antoine, Proue, and Vincent Tabeau scarcely drank a cup of coffee before starting to gather up gear.

Then the struggle with the mules began. Cold mornings were the worst, and just about every morning since the start had been cold.

The hollow was full of crashing sounds, shouts, and the grunts of packers being dragged around by mules.

Ted sized up Poche's disposition and decided to blindfold him. But that was easier said than done. Hammerheaded though he was, the mule could move his head like a snake. After a half-dozen tries, Ted got the blindfold on. When he put on the saddle blanket, Poche sagged as if a ton of weight had been dropped on him.

With as little flapping as possible, Ted set the saddle on. Poche humped and sucked in all the air he could hold, extending his stomach.

"You faker." Ted braced one foot against the mule's side and began to heave on the cinch until it seemed that it would cut the animal in two.

Poche let the air out. He tried his forward kick with his hind leg while Ted was loading the packs.

The boy removed the hobbles, got a good grip on the halter rope, and jerked the blindfold off. Poche looked at him mildly, as if to say, "Why did you bother with all the rigmarole? Anyone can see I'm docile."

Ted relaxed for an instant. It was then that Poche bolted straight into the mule herd, squealing and kicking. Ted grabbed the halter rope with both hands. His feet were off the ground for the first two jumps, and then he got them under him and tried to dig into the ground. It was like trying to hold a steamboat.

Poche crashed through the herd. Mules began to bray and kick. They trampled packs lying on the ground. Packers yelled angrily as they hung on to the plunging animals. Just when Ted thought he was going to lose his footing and be dragged on his belly, he got a chance to snub the rope around a tree. The moment Poche felt the pressure, he stopped. With his pack askew, he reached down and began to nibble grass.

Haler came striding up to Ted. "Haven't you learned to handle a mule yet, boy?"

It was on the tip of Ted's tongue to shout back, "Shut your big mouth!" But only his expression showed what he was thinking.

Considering everything, it was a fairly easy start the expedition made that morning. Soon after daylight the mules were strung out on the route the Delaware guides had selected.

But two days later, the Delawares left the expedition. They had been hired only to get Frémont well started along the new, central route toward the mountains.

Now Colonel Frémont chose the trail. In the face of increasing cold the caravan went up and down steeply pitched small hills, through broken gullies, and on across the windy flatlands. They saw more buffalo. Ned Kern, Cathcart, Godey, and the regular hunters were after them every day. Ted continued to watch the mules.

The day the expedition passed deserted brush huts of Pawnees, Ted decided that it was time to talk to his uncle again about hunting. He hailed Godey as he was passing with Ned Kern.

"I want to shoot a buffalo."

"There's plenty of time."

There would always be plenty of time, to hear Godey tell it.

"I'll be careful when I'm chasing them," Ted said.

"Oh yes, to be sure!" Godey waved his hands. "Everyone is careful while running buffalo. That is how they break their necks."

"He's going to have a whack at it someday, whether you like it or not," Kern said. "Why not give him the chance?"

"It is dangerous!" Godey protested.

"So is packing mules," Kern said. "I've never been run over by a buffalo, but I've been knocked end over appetite by mules. Take him along with us. We can watch out for him."

And that was how Ted found himself hunting the next day with Godey, Cathcart, Scott, Martin, and Ned Kern. They had spied their buffalo, a long line coming in

single file over a distant hill. Dismounted, the hunters
waited beside their horses in a shallow dip.

Ted gripped his rifle hard. The buffalo grew larger,
plodding straight toward the hunters.

"Keep to the outside," Godey warned. "Don't try to
get in the middle of everything."

Ted nodded. His mouth was too dry to speak. He
looked at the horse his uncle had lent him and hoped that
it knew its business. The buffalo were only a few hundred
yards away when they dipped out of sight in a swale.

"Now," Godey said, "everyone ride slowly at first."

They went forward at a walk, and then a trot. It
seemed that the earth had swallowed the buffalo. Riding
on the extreme right, with Godey beside him, Ted began to
fear that the buffalo had escaped down a gully.

Two great brown forms heaved into sight suddenly,
coming up from the swale. Captain Cathcart and Kern
yelled like Indians as they charged forward. The two buffalo stood stupidly for a moment, then whirled and ran.

When Ted rode over the crest and could see into the
swale, there seemed to be enough buffalo for everyone in
St. Louis. The whole bottom was filled with the huge,
jostling creatures. Ted heard Godey yell something, but he
didn't know what it was and he didn't care. He thun-
dered down the slope, straight toward the main mass of
buffalo. They were running before he reached them.

Someone shouted. Rifles boomed. Ted's horse
stretched out in a wild run. Ted was in the midst of running buffalo, with the thunder of hoofs all around him.

Dark, woolly shapes, twice as big as they had seemed at a distance, were bumping along beside him at incredible speed.

A bull crowded toward him, its massive shoulders working. The horse veered nimbly away, almost against another buffalo running on Ted's right. It occurred to him that he had done just what Godey had warned him not to do. But he couldn't stop, or even look behind him. He yelled and ran with the buffalo, too busy keeping his saddle to try a shot. How long he raced with them he didn't know. They began to scatter in little bands.

One bull was still near him and Ted swung his rifle in one hand to fire. He was so close that he expected the bull to go end over end when he shot but nothing happened.

Reloading posed a problem that Ted hadn't considered. His horse was galloping full tilt over uneven ground. He was trying to get powder into the barrel as it bobbed up and down with every surge of the horse, when his mount stumbled and almost fell. Ted dropped his rifle and grabbed the reins with both hands. Fifty yards beyond, he brought the horse to a stop. Running buffalo were scattered all around him. He couldn't see a rider anywhere. He turned back to retrieve his rifle.

The ground was churned. He wasn't sure how far he had gone after he dropped the rifle. Dust was hanging in the air as he searched for the weapon.

He saw it at last and dismounted. It was then that Godey came riding up. His expression was angry, and for a moment Ted was sure that he was in for it.

Godey saw the rifle on the trampled earth. He grinned suddenly. "Everyone has to learn."

As they rode back to where Godey had killed a fat buffalo cow, Ted said, "You're not going to tell the whole camp that I dropped my rifle after one shot?"

"You are alive, unharmed. I have nothing to tell anyone."

Ted kept thinking of how wild and wonderful it had been to ride among those buffalo. But the next time . . . First, he would stay on the outside of the herd, and second, he wouldn't drop his rifle.

He got his next chance at buffalo sooner than he expected, and without having to ride after them.

That same day a large herd of buffalo, running from some unknown danger, came thundering down on the mule train just as the expedition was going into camp. Men grabbed the lead ropes of the mules.

Gregorio, one of the Tulare Indians, rode out at the charging mass of buffalo, waving a blanket. Ted's heart was in his mouth for a few moments. It seemed that Gregorio would be swept under and trampled, but the herd turned away from him, roaring past the train not more than a hundred and fifty yards away.

The mules steadied down then. Shots broke out as men began to fire. Ted grabbed his rifle and stood beside Martin, who was kneeling. Their weapons boomed out together. The big bull that Ted was aiming at went down.

Martin grinned. "I think we both got that one. I aimed at its head. Where were you shooting?"

"At the biggest part of him, I guess. The shoulder."

They walked over and looked at the dead bull. He had been shot once through the lungs, and Martin, sure enough, had drilled him through the head.

"So you helped kill a buffalo," Godey said to his nephew that evening. "Now we won't have to worry about it, yes?"

A few days later a bitter snowstorm struck. The caravan halted shortly after noon, bringing the mules close to the fires.

Later, through snow that balled up on the hoofs of the shod mules, the expedition left the Smoky Hill Fork and turned south. For a while Ted and the others were kept busy knocking the snow from the shoes of the mules, so they could walk without limping. Then it warmed a little and the snow mushed down to where it was no longer a problem.

They reached the Arkansas River. Not long afterward, Ted saw his first truly wild Indians.

CHAPTER 3

Comanches

HERE THE ARKANSAS WAS wide and shallow, with weedy islands lying between its channels. Not far ahead was Chouteau's Island, named for a famous trader of the early fur-hunting days.

The expedition was on the Santa Fe Trail, a route marked by the wheels of Americans who had been trading with the villages of New Mexico since 1821.

One of Frémont's old hands, Captain Henry King, came hurrying along the route. "Indians up ahead! Comanches and Kiowas. Tighten up. Don't straggle, and don't let 'em run free in the pack train."

Preuss came by looking for the mule that was carrying some of his equipment. "Do you think there'll be trouble?" Ted asked.

"No," the German said absently, and rode on to find his precious gear.

The Comanches who met the train sometime later didn't look very peaceful to Ted. Some of them stopped to talk to Colonel Frémont and the scouts, while others came galloping down the line of mules, whooping and yelling.

They were as savage-looking people as Ted cared to see. Dark and broad, they rode as if they were part of their horses. Some of them wore buffalo robes that flapped behind them as they raced along. All of them were armed with strong, short bows and plenty of arrows.

Ted had heard that a Comanche riding full tilt could shoot arrows five times as fast as a man could fire a rifle. Watching the way the Indians rode, he didn't doubt it. He kept his rifle balanced across his legs, with his thumb on the hammer.

Suddenly, one of the wild riders plunged to a stop in front of him and shouted fiercely. Ted looked into the hard eyes of the Comanche and shook his head. The Indian shouted again. Ted shook his head. "Beat it!" he said.

Antoine came up. He spoke to the Comanche and made signs, pointing ahead, then pointing at Ted. The Indian's mood changed. He stared solemnly at Ted, made a sign, and rode away to join his howling companions.

"What did you tell him?"

"I told him you were the nephew of Godey." Antoine smiled. "And the adopted son of Kit Carson."

"What was he yelling about in the first place?"

"He said you were holding your rifle as if you didn't know he was a friend. He said you were afraid."

"He sure was right."

As they moved closer to the Indian camp, more riders came out to meet them. Some of them were Kiowas, whose record along the Santa Fe Trail made them more feared by small caravans than even Comanches or Apaches.

The expedition made ready to camp near Chouteau's Island, setting up about a half-mile from the Indians. Ted was wrestling the pack off Poche when Indian children came swarming into camp. The younger ones were jabbering, curious, poking at everything, until Antoine and Tabeau waved them back.

Many of the children were decked out with silver ornaments. Some of them wore coins in their hair.

Aloof from the scurry of younger children was a boy about Ted's age. In his right hand he held the lead rope to a mule. Tall, slender, solemn, he waited until Ted was alone. Then he led the mule forward. He pointed to Ted's rifle leaning against a pack, then pointed to the mule.

"You want to trade?"

The Indian didn't understand.

"Trade?" Ted repeated. He pointed. "That poor old beat-up mule for . . ." he indicated his gun ". . . my good rifle?"

The boy nodded. He thrust the rope toward Ted and reached toward the rifle.

"Not so fast!" Ted grabbed his rifle. He walked around the mule, scowling. The animal was gaunt and its back showed healing sores. Probably it had been picked up after some pack train had abandoned it.

Just two days before, Colonel Frémont had ordered

three mules turned free because they were failing. Ted knew this was not one of them, though it was in no better shape than those three had been.

Ted was not going to trade, but he wanted to get acquainted with the boy. He shook his head. "No good."

The Indian scowled. "Good!"

"No."

The Indian studied Ted carefully, and it was hard to tell what he was thinking. Finally, he led the mule away, looking for a trade elsewhere.

There was scarcely time to eat before adult Indians, both Comanche and Kiowa, arrived in great numbers to trade. They were more ceremonious than the children. They came in slowly, some of them riding, some of them afoot, leading mules and horses.

Antoine pointed out the Kiowa leader to Ted. His name was Little Mound, a tall man who squinted his eyes when he talked. Though his legs were bare to the cold evening, he wore a cape of black buffalo hide. Around his neck was a heavy string of shell ornaments. He wore high Apache moccasins.

While Little Mound and some of the other Indian leaders were talking to Frémont and Godey, Henry King and Charlie Taplin made an inspection of the camp to see that everything was stowed away under the canvases that were used nightly to cover the packs.

"They'll steal anything that's loose, boys," Taplin warned. "Keep your eyes open."

Antoine was sitting on a pile of packs, smoking his short pipe. He rubbed his scarred lip and looked at Ted.

"They take things, yes," he said, shrugging. "Stealing
to them is not wrong. Today we are friends. Tomorrow we
are enemies again, so they steal against the time when we
are enemies, which is almost always."

"Suppose they wanted to fight?" Ted asked.

"There will be no trouble. Even Indians do not fight
among themselves when there is trading to be done. Besides, their hearts are good now because they are on their
way to Big Timbers, where the Indian agent, Tom Fitzpatrick, will hold a council and give them gifts. For the
moment they are like tame wolves, friendly and happy, but
ready to tear your throat out if something goes wrong."

Tame wolves. That was a good description, Ted
thought. He looked at the stocky Comanches. They raided
trading caravans on the Santa Fe Trail. They butchered
stragglers as one might shoot prairie dogs, for fun. They
plundered the small ranches and towns of New Mexico,
taking loot and captives as they pleased.

Mission doors were sheathed with copper for protec-
tion against the fire arrows of Comanches. All these things
Ted knew from talking to his uncle.

Trading began near the main fire, in front of Colonel
Frémont's tent. Thomas Breckenridge, Josiah Ferguson,
and Henry Wise, Missourians who knew much about
mules, inspected the animals the Indians led forward, then
gave their opinions to Frémont and Godey.

In turn, the Indians inspected the horses the white
men wished to exchange for mules.

For a time there was much talk, a great deal of sign
language, and no results. Breckenridge and his companions

rejected every mule put up for trade. The Indians shook their heads at the horses. Both sides were setting forth the worst they had, to start the trading.

Other Indians with no animals to trade wandered through the camp, peering into tents, trying to lift the canvas covering the packs.

Three stalwart Comanches approached Antoine and Ted. In growling language they offered to trade brightly colored Mexican blankets.

Old Antoine indicated the packs and made sign talk. The Comanches grunted with disgust and moved on.

"What did you tell 'em?"

"I said we had nothing in the packs but tents." Antoine raised his forefingers, crossing the tips to indicate an Indian lodge.

Not far away young Julius Ducatel of Baltimore and Micajah McGehee were having a bad time trying to get rid of the same three Indians. Somewhat nervously, Ducatel had drawn his gold watch to look at the time, and now the Indians were trying to trade him out of the watch.

Up at the main fire, trading was picking up. Several mules and horses were exchanged. Then the Indians were suddenly reluctant to trade further. They kept pointing to the silver coins in their hair. Colonel Frémont said to Godey, "Tell them we have no silver, Alex. And say that when we reach Big Timbers, our other Indian friends will have many mules to trade."

That helped speed up business slightly, but Frémont was still left with a good many horses.

"Do they steal all those mules they've got?" Ted asked
Antoine.

"Some, yes," Antoine said. "Others they find after
the mules are turned loose, too weak to travel. Some they
take from wagons after they kill the traders."

And the Mexican blankets and jewelry—Ted wondered if they, too, had been taken as loot after some
bloody raid.

Among the half-naked children scampering about, he
saw two that didn't look like Indians. Their features were
finer, not nearly as broad as the general cast of the faces
around them.

"Did you see those two boys?"

Antoine nodded. "Mexican children, taken in a raid."

"What will happen to them?"

"They will grow up as Comanches."

"And never know the difference?"

"Perhaps some day. It is possible that, before they
grow up, they will be traded back to the Mexicans, but it
is unlikely that their parents are alive." Antoine was un-
disturbed. "Perhaps they are better off as Comanches."

"To fight against their own people?" Ted asked indignantly.

Antoine puffed his pipe. "That is a problem, yes." He
spread his hands. "But there is nothing we can do about
it. Perhaps Tom Fitzpatrick can do something, now that
he is the agent for all the Indians here."

The trading went on until dark. Then the white men
withdrew their horses and put them under guard, and also

doubled the watch on the mule herd. Gradually, the Indians left the camp.

The only thing reported stolen was one saddle blanket. That didn't seem like much, but Godey protested to Little Mound. Later, Henry Wise, who had gone to visit the Indian camp, reported that the chief was standing on a high bank above the Arkansas, lecturing his people on the evils of stealing from white men.

Ted had two hours of sleep before he was roused to stand guard. As he went dragging through the camp, yawning and blinking, he saw Preuss at work in his tent by candlelight. The map maker was bent over papers laid out on his folding table. Smoke from his pipe was hanging above his mop of curly hair.

Out on the cold plain near the mules, Ted heard yelling at the Indian camp. They were having a dance or some kind of celebration there. He hoped they weren't getting worked up to go on the war path.

Six men were standing watch over the mules. On the half-hour Lige Andrews made the rounds of the guards. He was a former Navy man who was on the trip to improve his health. He had lung trouble, and every now and then Ted could hear him stifling a cough.

Twice during Ted's watch, the Tulares, Joaquin and Gregorio, called softly from the dark, and then came silently out of the night to go prowling around the herd. Since they were not assigned to this watch, Ted guessed they were uneasy in the presence of the plains Indians, and unable to sleep.

The mules thumped about on hobbled feet. Grass was scarce here, as it was a common camping place.

Ted was leaning on his rifle, half-drowsing in spite of the cold, when he heard the sound of horses coming toward the herd. They were walking slowly. He crouched down, staring up at the skyline in an effort to sight the riders. It was too dark to see anything.

The horses stopped. Ted listened, hardly breathing. After a few moments he heard the horses moving again, going west. Then someone challenged sharply. It sounded like Dick Kern's voice.

Men answered in the gobbling Kiowa language. The riders moved on, going toward the river. For a while after that Ted was wide awake and alert.

Ned Kern had said that the expedition had traveled more than four hundred miles from Westport. In the dark, Ted thought he could feel all that wild and lonely space around him. Somewhere to the north a wolf howled, and then the pack set up a quavering, mournful song. Godey said you could tell what wolves were doing from the sound of their voices, but all Ted could get from the noise was a sense of sadness and loneliness.

It was the night of November 9, 1848.

CHAPTER 4

Sign Talk

IN THE MORNING THE expedition moved much earlier than usual. As the pack train strung out on the march, Indian riders loped over to join the white men.

Comanche and Kiowa children, who didn't look old enough to stay aboard a pony, came dusting up bareback. They yelled and tore around, showing off their horsemanship, until some of the mules grew uneasy and tried to bolt. After an old warrior shouted and raised his arm, the children calmed down.

Soon white men and Indians were all intermingled, as they rode through the dust.

A group of Kiowas began a wild song, full of ai-yai's and shouts. Tabeau, Proue, and some of the other Frenchmen joined in with them, whooping when the Indians whooped, grunting and chanting, doing their best to stay with the Kiowas.

"What are they singing?" Ted asked Antoine.

Antoine waved his hands. "Who knows? No one understands what a Kiowa says. It is a holiday. They are going to Big Timbers to see their great friend, Fitzpatrick. There will be dancing, feasting, presents. Perhaps that is what they are singing of."

Presently the Frenchmen began a *voyageur* song. Ted could understand most of that. It was a rollicking tale of wide rivers and life in the Northwest woods around the Great Lakes.

Not to be outdone, the Indians joined in. Now and then they got a word right, but most of their effort was howling and yipping. Before long, Antoine was grinning from ear to ear and Ted was laughing.

All along the train there were similar efforts to sing together in three different languages, and sometimes four. After a while Ted shook his head in amazement. On this day no one would ever think that the Kiowas and Comanches were the two tribes most dreaded by white men on the plains.

Out of the dust a rider on a calico pony fell in beside Ted. It was the same Indian boy who had tried to trade the mule for Ted's rifle. Ted greeted him with a raised right hand, palm outward.

The boy responded, saying nothing for a while as they rode along. At last he began to make signs, so rapidly and with such ease that Ted was lost in no time. From Godey and Antoine he had learned some sign talk, but the only thing he caught from the young Indian's motions was the sign for mule—both hands cupped above the ears, with the fingers dipping to indicate the movement of a mule's ears.

"Does he want to trade again?" Ted asked.

Antoine shook his head. "He says we are foolish to go into the mountains in winter. Everyone says it's a bad winter, much snow, no game to hunt. He says the mules will die and we will freeze in the deep snow."

"How does he know?"

"From the Arapahoes who were up there fighting Utes when the storms began."

"Do you think he's right?"

"About the snow, yes. But Colonel Frémont has been in snow before." Antoine sign-talked to the boy, and then translated for Ted. "He is Buffalo Hunter, a Kiowa. Four seasons ago he killed his first buffalo, and he has killed many since."

Ted stared at Buffalo Hunter with envy. Four years ago he couldn't have been more than ten or eleven years old, but Ted didn't doubt the truth of his claim. He knew that Indians were usually truthful when bragging about their deeds of valor. "Good!" he exclaimed to show his appreciation of the Kiowa's skill as a hunter.

"Good!" Buffalo Hunter agreed. He detailed some other exploit.

"He says he wounded a Pawnee in a fight last summer," Antoine translated. "A full warrior." He suppressed a smile. "But the man got away."

Ted studied Buffalo Hunter's short bow. It was as powerful as any he had seen adult Indians carrying. "Ask him about those Mexican kids we saw."

After a long exchange of signs, during which the

Kiowa appeared to be bored, Antoine explained, "He says he doesn't know where they were captured. They belong to Kills-the-Pawnee, one of the Comanches."

It was only natural, Ted thought, that an Indian would be little concerned with the problems of captives. Indian life on the plains was far different from a white man's way of living.

The three rode along in silence for a while. A sudden impulse struck Ted. He unbuckled his belt and slipped off the beaded case with its heavy knife. The case was Teton Sioux, while the knife itself was Spanish steel. Godey had brought it to Ted as a present when he returned from one of his western trips.

Reining over toward Buffalo Hunter, Ted offered him the knife and case. The Kiowa lad stared at him.

"Take it. It's a present."

Buffalo Hunter accepted the gift. He thrust it carelessly into his belt, hardly glancing at it. Soon, without a word of thanks or parting, he rode away.

"What was the matter with him?" Ted asked.

"Nothing. If you had given him twenty ponies, he would have tried not to show surprise. That's the Indian way."

"He might have said thanks at least."

Antoine smiled. "In time you will learn about Indians. That is, if you do not become careless some day and give them that fine head of hair."

"You're not much help, Antoine."

All day the Indians traveled with the expedition. That night they camped with the white men. Once more Little

Mound made a long speech about honesty. Godey and a
few others caught the general drift of it, but when it came
to following the words one by one, Godey shook his head.

With a sly look at Preuss, who was fussing over a map
case nearby, Godey said, "It would be easier to understand
German than Kiowa, I think."

For a moment Preuss pretended not to hear, and then
he said, "That is French he is talking, which only wild men
speak."

Campfires lifted against the clear sky. The Indians
had plenty of meat, which they shared with the whites.
There was feasting at every fire. Ted observed how the Indians ate their meat, seared on the outside, hot and red and
dripping on the inside.

The Frenchmen, and most of the veterans of Frémont's company, preferred their meat the way the Indians
ate it. Back in the Smoky Hills, Godey and some of the
others, including Ned Kern, had eaten the roasted entrails
of a buffalo cow. They said it was wonderful, but Ted
hadn't sampled it.

Tonight Ted tried roasted hump meat the Indian way.
The taste was all right, but the meat was too hot for his
mouth. He nibbled at it, waiting for it to cool a little. He
watched Captain Cathcart and Colonel Frémont sitting
at a fire with Little Mound and some of the lesser chiefs.
Cathcart was in his glory. All day long he had stayed
among the Kiowas.

Now Captain Cathcart of a titled Scottish family was
eating meat Indian style, with the juices smeared into his
mustache and running down into his sandy beard.

Dainty manners just didn't fit out here, Ted decided. He began to eat his hump meat like everyone else, letting the juices run where they would. One Indian habit that he didn't care to follow, however, was wiping his greasy hands in his hair. He wiped them on his pants instead. After weeks of dust and campfire grime, his pants were so dirty that a little more grease didn't matter.

He went looking for Buffalo Hunter. Hungry dogs eyed him as he made his way through the camp. There seemed to be a thousand of them, growling, snapping at each other, lying beyond the fires, waiting for someone to throw them a bone. Ted was wary of the dogs as he went along chewing his buffalo meat, but he put on a bold front and they got out of his way.

He came to a fire where Indians were dancing. A clear moon was shining on the wild scene. Bare arms and legs gleamed like old bronze, as the dancers shuffled and stomped. An old man chanted in a piping voice and thumped a drum. Shell necklaces clattered. Hammered coins clinked. Moccasined feet thumped. Brown-faced men in black buffalo robes stood solemnly with folded arms, watching the dancers.

Suddenly the dancers stopped. A tall warrior stepped forward, tapping his scarred chest. He began to tell of some heroic deed. Now and then his listeners applauded him, growling, "Howh! Howh!"

It would be a mighty poor occasion to get up and tell some big lie, Ted decided. The audience probably was waiting for the warrior to slip from the truth.

Ted moved on slowly. He found Buffalo Hunter

watching a dance at another fire. The Kiowa boy was wearing the knife Ted had given him. Ted pretended not to notice it. In the simplest kind of sign language—by pointing his forefinger at Buffalo Hunter, his thumb at his own breast, and then pointing over his shoulder—Ted asked the Indian to go with him.

They walked over to some packs where Jackson, Colonel Frémont's cook, was sitting. Ted pointed toward the mule herd. He made the mule sign. He indicated Buffalo Hunter's bow, and then made the shooting sign, an easy matter of using his hands as if releasing an arrow.

What he meant to convey was that he wanted to learn some sign language, but before he could go farther, Buffalo Hunter made the shooting sign and looked toward the mules, puzzled.

"No, no!" Ted cried. "I don't want you to shoot a mule!"

It took a little time, but finally he got across the idea that he wished to learn some Kiowa. After that, things came easier. Ted would point to something, say the name of the object, and then look questioningly at Buffalo Hunter. The Kiowa would give the Indian name of the object, if it had one. Then he would make the sign for it.

Right there Ted despaired of learning the Kiowa language. It was too tongue twisting. But the signs were something else. Almost all of them were easily understood, because they bore resemblance to the object indicated.

He had trouble with "dog." When he pointed to a dog, Buffalo Hunter extended his first two fingers downward in a V and made a dragging motion.

It didn't make sense.

Jackson was watching them in fascination. He, too, was puzzled for a while about the dog sign, and then his face brightened. "Mistuh Ted, he means the dogs drag those stick things behind them."

Travois, of course! It was the Indian way of transporting lodge skins and other baggage on a framework stretched between two poles, which were usually dragged behind a horse. Though Ted had never seen a dog *travois*, he had heard of them.

While Jackson and Ted were grinning at each other, Buffalo Hunter looked at them calmly and said, "Travois."

"I'll be dogged!" Jackson said. "Your friend there sure is a smart one, Mistuh Ted."

Verbs were the easiest of all, Ted decided, once you could get across the idea of the action you wanted described. Ted got up and walked a few paces. Buffalo Hunter made the walking sign, extending his hands and advancing one over the other to indicate steps.

Ted did a few stomps to indicate dancing. The Kiowa held his hands upward, palms facing each other, and then worked his hands up and down, showing the motion of an Indian dancer.

"Why, I think I could catch on pretty fast," Ted said to Jackson.

Jackson nodded. "You is young, Mistuh Ted. That's the time to learn, sure enough."

Too soon, it was time for Ted to go on guard duty. He gave the signs to Buffalo Hunter, "you" and "me"— "friends."

The Kiowa boy nodded. He put one hand on Ted's shoulder, and for the first time since they had met, he smiled.

While he stood his lonely watch that night, Ted kept practicing the sign talk he had learned. He wished that he could spend a long time with the Indians. He and Buffalo Hunter could have fun together.

CHAPTER 5

Big Timbers

THE NEXT DAY THE Indians left the slow mule train behind and hurried on to Big Timbers.

Riding through the dust beside Ted, Godey said, "There will likely be five or six thousand of them at the council. You see, old Tom Fitzpatrick is trying to patch up a peace treaty between all the tribes out here." He shook his head doubtfully.

Though he had never seen Fitzpatrick, Ted had heard much of him. One of the most respected of Mountain Men, Fitzpatrick had spent many years in the West. It was said that Indians accepted his word because he had never lied to them.

"You don't seem to think he'll have any luck making a treaty," Ted said.

Godey shrugged. "It's winter now. No grass for ponies.

The Indians are willing to be peaceable. But when spring comes and the grass grows again . . ."

"You mean they'll go back to killing traders and raiding wherever they can?"

"Indians are Indians. They've got to chase buffalo to live. Warring is part of their life, too. Nobody is going to make farmers out of them just by telling them it's a good way to live." Godey shook his head. "But if anyone can hold them to a peace, Tom Fitzpatrick is the man."

Under warming skies the caravan crossed and re-crossed the Arkansas River. There was ice along the edges of the stream. Ted kept looking ahead for mountains, but all he saw was the horizon.

The expedition passed the heavy wagons of the noted trader, Ceran St. Vrain. They were loaded with goods for the council at Big Timbers. Some of the mules were in bad shape, and some of the wagons were straggling.

St. Vrain himself was on ahead at Big Timbers. Both he and Fitzpatrick had left with the wagon train a few weeks before the fourth expedition started from Westport.

Ted watched the shouting wagoneers, urging their mules to drag the wagons through heavy sand. Wagon travel, he decided, was not for him.

The marks of Indians on the road were heavier than ever. Thousands of ponies had passed. It seemed that all the Indians of the plains were on their way to Big Timbers.

Through the winter haze, Ted saw the beginning of what looked like an enormous grove of trees. As the expedition drew closer to the trees, Ted could tell that the grove was the biggest stand of cottonwoods they had encountered anywhere on the Arkansas.

This was Big Timbers, a favorite wintering place of Cheyennes, Apaches, Arapahoes, Kiowas, and Comanches.

"She is a big grove," Antoine said. "For maybe twenty-five miles we have trees. Good shelter. Many Indians, too."

He had scarcely finished speaking when they came to a camp of Arapahoes. Brown children clad only in breechclouts and moccasins came running.

"They think we are traders, with many fine things in the packs," Antoine said.

Poche had developed a dislike of Indians and Indian ponies. He was given to kicking and biting when anything with an Indian smell came too close to suit him. He bared his teeth as an Arapaho boy trotted beside him, trying to lift the canvas on his pack.

Before Ted could yell a warning, Poche whirled and bared his teeth to crunch the young Indian's arm. The boy jumped away just in time. The mule's strong teeth snapped like a beaver trap within inches of his wrist.

The young Arapaho fell backward over a log as he retreated. His companions whooped with laughter. Afterward they stayed well away from Poche.

In a pleasant park among the trees, the expedition prepared to camp. Some of the Indian boys were still hanging around when Ted began to unload his mules. He thought it a good time to practice his sign language, so he signaled, "That mule—bad—kill."

The young Arapahoes laughed, pointing to the boy

who had gone too close to Poche. One of them made a sign meaning a chopped-off arm, and that sent them into even louder mirth.

Trading began as soon as the white men set up camp. Colonel Frémont and Godey had gone on to confer with Tom Fitzpatrick, who was camped in the very midst of the huge gathering of Indians.

The Arapahoes proved to be tough traders. They were not anxious to part with their mules.

Doc Kern had more luck than anyone.

On guard at a mound of packs, Ted watched the doctor treating an Indian who had sore eyes.

Ned Kern said to his brother, "Don't be so casual about it, Ben. You've got to put on a little show. When we told them you were a medicine man, they expected some kind of magic out of you."

"I'm a doctor, not a magician." Doc Kern peered into the inflamed eye of a scarred Arapaho with graying braids. "I can give only a little temporary relief in this case."

"Make a show of it then!" Ned said. "You're not treating some clerk back in Philadelphia, you know. Be a medicine man."

"I'm a doctor!" his brother said stiffly. He did unbend a little, however. Before he put some drops in the Indian's eyes, he looked at the sky and raised the bottle and spoke loudly in Latin.

The circle of Indians around the afflicted man watched in silence, as if they were weighing the powers of this white medicine man.

Doc Kern motioned ceremoniously with the bottle in all four directions. "This is foolish," he muttered.

"Wonderful!" Ned Kern said. "Don't forget to motion toward the earth with it."

Doc Kern put the medicine in the Indian's eyes, and a few moments later the Arapaho began to make a speech to his friends.

"What's he saying?" Ted asked Antoine.

"He's telling them he's cured."

The Indians seemed impressed, but there was no rush forward to seek the services of the white medicine man. Then the man who had already been treated poked his stomach with both hands and made the "bad" sign.

Doc Kern gave him some powders folded into paper, and had Raphael Proue explain when to take them. The Arapaho was happy. He presented the doctor with a mule.

Ned Kern laughed. "Now you're getting somewhere."

"I'm losing all my professional pride, you mean," Doc grumped, but there was a trace of a smile on his lips as he dipped into his supply of medicines again.

He made motions over a fire, while the Indians watched him raptly. Then he spoke in Latin and opened his hand. Bluish flames jetted up from the fire as the chemicals in his hand sprinkled down.

The Arapahoes fell back quickly, holding their hands over their open mouths.

"Now you're a full-fledged member of the medicine man's lodge, Big Timbers Chapter," Ned Kern said. He kept his face straight, but Ted could see that he was ready to burst out laughing.

From then on, the Arapahoes treated Dr. Kern with great respect. He could have traded the buffalo robes right off their backs, had he been willing to take advantage of them. So many of them leaped forward, wishing to hug him, that he had to retire to his tent before he was overwhelmed.

After dark a group of Indians began a dance. They waved their bows as they stamped around the fire. Silver foxtails fastened to their breechclouts bobbed in the firelight, as they circled and shouted.

"They're going out to fight the Pawnees and steal ponies," Antoine explained.

"I thought winter was a bad time for fighting."

"Not for the younger ones. Perhaps they wish to be married. Then they must have ponies to give the father of the girl. Is that not what you plan to do when you get to California?"

Ted grinned sheepishly. "Naw! You know better than that. I've got no time for girls. I may become a Mountain Man."

"So?" Antoine sucked at his pipe. It was out. He went to the nearest fire and picked up a hot coal to light the pipe again. He came back and setled down on the packs. "A Mountain Man, eh? Then you must marry an Indian girl. I saw one tonight over there . . ."

"Never mind!"

Buffalo Hunter came from the darkness and touched Ted's arm. Slowly, so that Ted could understand, he made

signs. After the sun came up, tomorrow, there would be a
meeting—Ted, Buffalo Hunter, and other Kiowas.

To be sure that he had it right, Ted asked Antoine.

"Yes, there will be a little council. You are invited.
There will be feasting, and then the Kiowas will choose a
beautiful girl for you to marry."

Ted gave Buffalo Hunter a startled look. "Aw! He
didn't say that last."

Antoine laughed.

"Maybe we won't be here," Ted said.

Antoine nodded. "I think so. The Colonel wishes to
talk a great deal with Fitzpatrick about the mountains. We
will be here another day."

The Kiowa came again the next morning, shortly
after Ted had eaten breakfast. He beckoned. They walked
away from camp, and then Buffalo Hunter began to trot.
Soon they were joined by two more young Kiowas, and a
third one came racing through the trees.

All of the Indians were carrying their weapons. They
ran tirelessly, leaping over logs, ducking around the enormous trunks of old cottonwoods. Ted fancied himself as a
runner, but he soon realized that his heavy, clumping boots
were poorly matched against the light moccasins of his
companions.

He caught his second wind. It was easier then, but he
was glad when at last the Kiowas stopped in a hollow at
the edge of the grove. Two other young Indians were already there. A fire was burning under a brass kettle where
meat was boiling.

Giant dead cottonwoods mingled with new growth

around the council place. Piles of whitened tree limbs were strewn about from some previous time when Indians had broken them from the trees to feed the bark to their ponies.

Ted settled down with the Kiowas around the fire. Though he had eaten not long before, the odor of meat in the boiling pot was tempting. Buffalo Hunter rose and made a short speech.

From what Ted could catch of the gestures, he knew that the Kiowa was telling the others that the white boy was a friend. He gathered, too, that Buffalo Hunter was the leader of the little group.

The spirit of the whole affair caught hold of Ted. He almost forgot that he was among Indians, hundreds of miles from St. Louis. This was sort of like stealing away to the woods with a group of boys his own age to roast a possum and mud-bake potatoes in the coals of the fire.

One of the Indians lit a long-stemmed pipe. He made motions with it, puffed smoke in four directions, then passed it on. Ted watched carefully the motions and the ceremony involved. When the pipe came to him, he did as he had seen the others do.

For a moment he thought he was going to strangle. Some of the smoke dribbled from his nose. He was on the verge of coughing the pipe clear over into the piles of whitened limbs. Ted barely managed to keep a straight face. He passed the pipe on to Buffalo Hunter, and gulped a few breaths of pure air into his lungs.

The smoking ceremony completed, one by one, the Kiowas rose to talk. It was all in sign language. After he caught the drift of things, Ted was startled. It was just like the bragging councils of their elders.

Buffalo Hunter's group of young Indians was going after Pawnees as soon as the meeting at Big Timbers was finished. They would walk until they found a Pawnee camp. Then they would creep in by night and steal horses. If pursued, they would fight and kill their pursuers.

Buffalo Hunter was the last to speak. His talk was shorter than any of the others. Near the end, Ted realized that Buffalo Hunter was inviting him to go along on the raid.

Ted was worried. He knew they considered it a great honor to invite him. He couldn't go, of course, but how to tell his friends that without offending them was a problem.

If they could understand English—but they couldn't.

Buffalo Hunter sat down. The Indians looked at Ted, waiting for him to speak. For a few moments, as Ted stood before them, he couldn't think of a single sign. He wanted to blurt out in English the reasons why he could not go.

Then he began to remember. Slowly at first, and then with more confidence, he used his hands. "I see friends together in council. Hunters. Pawnee hunters. Friends. Steal many ponies."

He shook his head. He made the sign for tears, meaning that he was sad. He made the signs for white men, mules, and mountains, and pointed to himself.

They understood. He had to go with the white men to the mountains.

When Ted sat down, the Kiowas shook their heads,

talking among themselves. At first he thought they were angry with him, but one of them sign-talked, saying that the mountains were bad, cold. Mules would die. White men would shiver and die. Mountains bad. The other Kiowas agreed.

Suddenly the whole nature of the meeting changed. The Indians began to laugh and joke. Buffalo Hunter speared a piece of meat from the pot with his knife and offered it to Ted.

Everyone began to eat then, dipping into the pot with knives, sticks, and fingers. The meat was tender and delicious, though Ted thought that it might have tasted a little better with salt; but that didn't keep him from eating as much as anyone else.

The stew was soon gone. Relaxed, their stomachs full, the Indians began to belch, which was a mark of politeness indicating that they had enjoyed the meal. Ted swallowed all the air he could hold. When his stomach rolled, he let loose a resounding belch that surprised even him.

His companions looked at him admiringly.

After a time someone kicked dirt on the fire. Another Kiowa picked up the kettle. They went back toward the middle of the grove, the Indians dropping away one by one until only Ted and Buffalo Hunter were left.

Haler was the first man Ted saw in camp. "Well, where have you been?" Haler asked, staring at Buffalo Hunter. "We're going to move on, you know, and you would have been left behind."

"I guess I could have caught up," Ted said. He turned

his back on Haler and thanked Buffalo Hunter for the feast
of antelope meat.

The Kiowa shook his head at the antelope sign. He
gave the sign of the *travois*.

Dog! Ted swallowed hard as he watched Buffalo
Hunter walk away.

CHAPTER 6

Tom Fitzpatrick

THAT AFTERNOON THE EXPEDITION went up the river a few miles to camp in a grassy bottom not far from Tom Fitzpatrick's lodge.

Since arriving at Big Timbers, Colonel Frémont and Godey had spent much of their time with Fitzpatrick, though Godey complained that they actually hadn't had much chance to talk to him because he was so busy with his Indian charges.

From all sides came more warnings of impassable snow and extreme cold in the mountains. Ted came in from gathering firewood to find a tall, bush-bearded trapper telling Charlie Taplin and King that they were crazy to go into the mountains.

The man was warming himself at a fire, resting his

hands on the muzzle of a stubby rifle. He was as dark as an Indian. He was a talkative trapper.

"The Colonel, he says to me, 'Mr. Lane, how about you guidin' me through the San Juans?' So I told him there ain't but a few—maybe like Old Bill Williams—as knows their way around that country."

Lane turned around to roast the other side of his pants at the fire. Ted figured if he got too close to the flames, the grease on his buckskins would ignite like gunpowder.

"I been talking to Injuns and trappers, and they say this is the worst year for snow since '41. Them Northern Lights been flickering like a forest fire over the mountains, and that's a sure sign of terrible weather. Another thing, Frémont, he don't want to go by no regular way. He figures to explore himself out a new way. That don't make good sense. No sir! Not in winter it don't."

Lane gulped coffee Taplin had given him. It was fresh off the fire and hot enough to scorch a hole in leather, but it didn't seem to bother him.

"So I says, 'No sir, Colonel, I sure do thank you for the honor, but this here young'un aims to stay close to buffalo land during the winter.' You know what the Colonel did? He just laughed." Lane shook his head. He drank the rest of the coffee.

Ted expected to see steam come out of his ears. But nothing happened, except that some of the coffee grounds stuck in Lane's beard.

He rubbed them away with a swipe of his ragged sleeve. "Now if I was Colonel Frémont, I'd go up the Purgatoire and on to Taos, and then steer this here pack train down toward the Gila and . . ."

"We don't want to go that way," Taplin said. "This outfit's looking for a railroad route straight through the mountains."

Lane laughed. "When steamcars start puffing through them San Juans, I'll say, 'Bill Lane, you've done lived too long.' Then I'll just curl up and die. You know something, boys? I figure to live another hundred years."

Some of the listeners laughed. Some were thoughtful. Ted was irritated. He didn't care for Lane saying that Colonel Frémont didn't know what he was doing. Alex Godey had complete trust in Colonel Frémont's ability to take an expedition anywhere, and that was good enough for Ted.

After Lane left, Ted asked Breckenridge, "Wasn't he just a big windbag?"

"Sounded like it, but he ain't altogether that. His trouble is he just don't know Colonel Frémont very well."

"Why do we need a guide at all?"

"Where we're headed is strange country to all of us. Even part way out on the plains, we had the Delawares, remember?"

That was right. Every day the Delawares had traveled a beeline, Ted recalled, knowing exactly where they were going; but after they turned back, the expedition had zigzagged until it reached the Arkansas.

If Lane didn't care to tackle the mountains, Ted guessed that Colonel Frémont would find someone with courage enough to be the guide. Disgusted with Lane's

talk, Ted saddled one of Godey's horses and rode over to
have a look at Tom Fitzpatrick.

About twenty Indians were in council with the old
Mountain Man. He was making them presents of awls,
sugar in little stone containers, vermilion, and strouds of
red wool.

Fitzpatrick was a lean man, crinkle-eyed and ruddy
from the winds and snows and blistering heat of far
places. His hair was snow white. Godey said that it had
turned that way in a single night, after a narrow escape
from Gros Ventre Indians.

Because one hand was mangled from an old accident
with a rifle that exploded, some tribes called him Broken
Hand. Others called him the One Talk Man, because he
spoke with a straight tongue.

Ted leaned against a tree and watched the gift-giving.
Fitzpatrick looked tired. No sooner did he present gifts to
one group of Indians, than another bunch moved forward
promptly from the hundred or more waiting near the lodge.

Off to one side, Frémont, Godey, and Henry King
were conferring with two Arapahoes who kept shaking their
heads.

Ted wondered if Frémont was trying to hire the two
as guides. He saw one of the Arapahoes point west and
make the "bad" sign. Afraid of the mountains, Ted
guessed.

Everyone seemed to be giving warnings about the
mountains, and so far, Ted hadn't even seen anything
higher than one of the bluffs near St. Louis.

He soon grew tired of the council, which promised to

go on forever. As he led Godey's horse away, some of the
waiting Indians turned to admire it. A huge Arapaho gave
it a hard slap on the rump, and laughed when the animal
jumped and almost bowled Ted over.

Instead of returning to camp, Ted rode west until he
was clear of the trees. The sparse buffalo grass was quiver-
ing before a cold wind, and there was a feel of snow in the
air. He stopped on a bluff to see if he could make out the
mountains.

As far as he could see, the country ahead was dead-
looking. An overcast sky and a haze obscured the mountains. The way it appeared, there could have been plains
stretching from where he was on to California.

Across the river he saw five Indians coming in from a
hunt. They rode humped in their crude saddles on scraggly
ponies that walked tiredly. He saw them looking toward
him, and he wondered how it would have been if he had
encountered them alone far out on the plains.

He was glad to put his back to the wind and return
to the shelter of the camp. There he learned that Ike
Cooper and Amos Andrews had decided to quit the expedition and return to the States. Andrews' son, Lige, was
going on in spite of his bad lungs.

Two hairy trappers in filthy buckskins and ragged
Mexican blankets had just arrived in camp. They were
wolfing down antelope meat that Billy Bacon had given
them.

"Whar at is Frémont?" one of them asked.

Bacon explained that he was with Fitzpatrick.

"They wish to go with us," Antoine told Ted. The old

Frenchman had put his buckskins away and was now clothed in a white woollen coat that reached below his knees. "I think all they want is someone to take them to California to steal mules."

"They've got horses. Why do they want to go all the way to California just to steal a few mules?"

"A few! If I know them, they wish to steal hundreds of mules to bring here and even to St. Louis for selling. In California the mules and horses grow like buffalo, wild and free. Someone owns them, of course, but he cannot use them all, or even watch them. Everyone steals mules from California. I have thought of doing so myself."

"Did you ever?"

Antoine grinned. "Not yet."

"It's a long way to drive them."

"Oh yes! Sometimes they all die on the desert. Sometimes the Indians steal them. It is never simple, or there would be even more people stealing mules."

Godey and Colonel Frémont returned while the two visitors were still eating. When they asked Frémont about joining the expedition, he told them he had all the men he needed.

The trappers got their horses and started on down the river. Ted heard one of them say, "That Frémont, Bill, he don't look like he's got sense enough to lead that pack train nowhere anyway."

On one of the mules that Godey had brought from the Indian camp was a buffalo-hide lodge. Ted helped unload it. The dark hides were remarkably soft and pliable.

"This one has been well used," Godey explained.

"Smoke from the lodge fire cures the skins so they don't shrink or dry out stiff after a wetting."

"Are we going to put it up right away?"

Colonel Frémont overheard the question. "Not tonight, Ted." He looked at the sky. "Before long, it will be most welcome." He smiled suddenly. "I understand the young Kiowas adopted you."

"I had a meeting with them, but I don't think they adopted me into the tribe."

"Make friends with Indians whenever you can."

There was always a driving, restless sort of energy in Colonel Frémont, even in his speech. He saw everything that was going on around the camp, but he never stayed long in one place. Now he strode away suddenly to his tent, stopping only to read the thermometers set on stakes well removed from any fire site.

CHAPTER 7

Bent's Fort

Tom Fitzpatrick rode with the expedition when it made its next move up the Arkansas. A bitter wind was blowing. As the trees of Big Timbers fell behind, the land ahead became gray and dismal, with the sky still threatening snow.

"Soon you will see the big fort of St. Vrain and Bent," Antoine promised. "Except for Fort Union, nowhere in the West will you see anything like this one."

Ted buttoned his woollen coat against the sharp bite of the wind. "It's in the trees, like the big Indian camp, I suppose."

"There are no trees, just the small bluffs and the river. For many years it has been a great place for trading with thousands of Indians."

Doc Kern came by on one of the mules he had secured from the Arapahoes, in exchange for calomel and Seidlitz powders. It was a fine-looking animal, but it had a wobbly, stumbling gait.

"You make no bargain with that mule, I think," Antoine called to Kern.

"She'll be all right when she learns where to put her feet," Kern replied, and rode on.

They began to cross the ice-edged Purgatoire River, a small stream with moss-scummed banks. Ted and Antoine grinned at each other as they watched the floundering efforts of Doc Kern's mule. It crossed all right, but going up the far bank where the footing was good, the mule fell suddenly.

Its nose came down like a hammer stroke and its legs seemed to fly out to the sides. Before it could roll and pin him, Doc Kern stepped out of the saddle. Freed of its rider, the mule exploded. It lunged to its feet, tore the reins from Doc Kern's hand, and went braying and bucking down the line of pack animals.

Two or three riders made an effort to intercept it, but the mule veered away and headed north. The incident set off some of the pack mules. Poche reached out and bit a big blue mule on the right. The blue mule kicked the one behind it.

For a few moments one whole section of the pack train was a tumult of braying, kicking, squealing, angry animals. A sack of cooking utensils flew loose and landed on the neck of a mule that was behaving itself. That touched the animal off. He tried to climb over the mule ahead.

When order was restored, the back part of the train hurried on to overtake the front section. During the difficulties, Godey galloped out on his horse and caught Doc Kern's saddle mule.

Kern resumed his saddle gingerly. Later, he stripped the gear off the mule and turned it loose to wander back to the Indians.

When Ted got his first view of Bent's Fort he was impressed. The structure sat on a level plateau above the Arkansas, grim and solid, with round towers rising at two corners. Even from a distance the place looked big enough to hold an army.

Ted half expected to see soldiers emerge from the gate, but as they drew closer to the fort there was still no activity. No cannon fired a welcome signal. No bugle sounded. No flag was flying above the walls.

"Some fort," Ted grumbled. "Where's the people?"

"Now only a few," Antoine said. "They stay by the fire and tell big lies."

It seemed to Ted that Big Timbers would have been a much better place for a trading post than this lifeless area, but he guessed the fort must have been located here because of the open ground all around it, which would make a sneak attack against the walls almost impossible.

The expedition camped across the river from the fort. Colonel Frémont, Godey, and Fitzpatrick rode on, and Ted tried to keep an eye on them to see if the gates of Bent's Fort would open to receive them.

Busy with the chores of unpacking and caring for the mules, he couldn't watch the riders all the time. They were close to the fort when he had last looked, and then he had to help Antoine with a mule that was trying to roll with its pack still on.

When he had a chance to look across the river again, the riders had disappeared.

The huge, silent structure had gulped them up, and there was still no sign of life over there. Ted decided that he would see for himself what Bent's Fort was like, just as soon as he could get away from his duties.

The chance to investigate the place didn't come early, because Ted became interested in helping put up the Indian lodge that Frémont had gotten at Big Timbers. While others were unpacking the hides, Ted went with Antoine and Tableau to find lodge poles.

That was no easy matter. Though there was still some timber at the campsite, the few pieces suitable for lodge poles were green and heavy. Hacked stumps and the burned marks of old fire sites showed that many travelers had camped here before.

"It is the same all along the Arkansas," Antoine complained. "Men who go with wagons make fires as high as a horse to boil one cup of coffee. When the trees are all gone . . ." He shrugged. "Well, I will be in California then."

They dragged the poles back to camp with a mule that rolled its eyes in terror, sidled, and tried to bolt away from the strange weight behind it.

Once the poles were leaned against each other to form a cone, the hides were stretched around the framework. This was not as simple as Ted had thought. It was ten feet

up to the top of the lodge. Ted stood on a horse to drag the
hides up. That worked well, until someone accidentally
touched the horse's tender flank.

The animal shied. Ted half fell and half jumped,
almost landing on top of Saunders Jackson, who steadied
him and kept him from reeling backward into someone's cooking fire.

"I dunno about these silly Indian houses," Jackson
said, shaking his head. But his attitude changed soon afterward.

When the hides were stretched and pegged down at
the bottom, with a small fire burning in a pit in the middle
of the interior, the lodge was a warm place. Smoke
drifted up through the hole where the poles were crossed
at the top.

"Hmn!" said Jackson. "This is some bigger and
warmer than those flimsy linen things."

There were still hides to spare. Tabeau and Antoine
lashed them to the inside of the poles, until all around the
interior there was a wall about five feet high. Now the place
was still warmer.

All his chores completed, Ted decided to ride over to
the fort. He was just starting when he saw a lone Indian
coming up the river. It was Buffalo Hunter. Ted rode out
to meet him.

The Kiowa's legs were bare. Around his shoulders he
wore a blue blanket. The two boys greeted each other,
and then Ted motioned toward camp, inviting Buffalo
Hunter to eat.

The Indian shook his head. He got down, taking a

buckskin bag from his pony. He signaled for Ted to join him. Then he presented Ted with the bag. Inside were four pairs of new moccasins with parfleche soles. The rest of the bag was filled with deer hair.

Puzzled by this last, Ted gave no sign of confusion. He thanked his friend as best he could, and then it occurred to him that perhaps Buffalo Hunter would like to go with him to the fort. The Kiowa nodded agreement.

They raced each other when they reached the plateau where the fort sat. Ted's mule was no match for the Indian pony. Laughing, their eyes running from the rush of cold wind, they reached the double gate in the face of the east wall. Ted hammered with his rifle butt on the iron-plated barrier.

Close in, the walls looked twice as high as an Indian lodge. The adobe blocks had been mud-plastered, but in places the plaster was peeling, showing the joints of the big blocks.

After a long time they heard a stirring somewhere inside. Then a bearded face looked out from the wall above them. The man shouted something in English, but with such a thick French accent that Ted couldn't understand him.

In French, Ted yelled back, "We want in!"

"There is no business here now. Go away."

"I want to see my uncle."

"Who is he?"

"Alexis Godey."

"Ah!" The bearded face broke into a smile. "That is

different, then. Go to the corral behind. It is of a too great exertion to open the heavy gates before you."

They rode around to the west side of the fort, where a long corral, also of adobe blocks, was backed against the higher walls of the fort. The gate to the corral was unlocked. Inside were the horses of Colonel Frémont and the others.

From a high opening in the wall of the fort, the Frenchman let down a ladder on a rope. Ted and Buffalo Hunter climbed up, emerging on a graveled roof.

"I will take you to your uncle," the bearded man said, drawing up the ladder. "Though it is a conference of great importance which is going on, I will—"

"Never mind. There is no hurry. May we look around the fort?"

The Frenchman looked doubtfully at Buffalo Hunter, and then he said, "I think it will be all right, if you do not enter the rooms."

The place was a maze. Some of the inner buildings were two-storied and stacked haphazardly. There was a *placita* or courtyard, onto which all the windows of the rooms opened, and beyond that a wagon yard.

Ted and Buffalo Hunter worked their way over rooftops and through narrow passages, until they reached the east wall of the fort.

From there they could look across at the campfires of the expedition, and then on to the limitless plains. Buffalo Hunter pointed out a band of antelope skimming away, so distant that Ted could barely make them out.

Directly above the main gate was a flat-roofed watchtower, with openings on all four sides.

"Ah!" said Ted, when he saw the telescope mounted in the middle of the room. He swung it to point at Frémont's camp. When he had the glass in focus, he saw Haler and Captain Cathcart standing near the Indian lodge, waving their hands and talking as they examined the lodge.

He motioned for Buffalo Hunter to take a look. The Kiowa peered through the telescope. Then he leaped away from it with a startled grunt. He didn't know how the glass could bring the campsite so close.

He went around and peered into the big end of the telescope, as if he could find what he had just seen. Then he stared at the distant camp. Again he took a look through the small end of the telescope and once more he drew away in alarm.

Ted focused the glass on the antelope. They had stopped to browse on a bluff. When Buffalo Hunter looked at them through the powerful instrument, he reached for an arrow. He was putting the notch to his bowstring as he drew back from the telescope.

With an expression of awe and anger he again examined the big end of the glass, to see if the antelope were hidden there.

"Far see," Ted said in sign language. He was afraid to try to explain any more than that, for fear of getting Buffalo Hunter more confused than he already was.

After a while, Buffalo Hunter seemed to catch on. He lost his awe of the instrument, and couldn't get enough of looking through it, but still he grunted his astonishment each time he found something new to look at.

While the Kiowa was thus absorbed, Ted examined the arms hanging on the walls of the room. The purpose of Indian lances he could understand and the rack of heavy muskets. But he couldn't figure out what use the swords hanging here would be to a defender trying to fight attackers at the gate below.

There was a small swivel gun, dismounted and shoved in a corner with some lengths of rope. The little cannon, Ted guessed, was more useful for making noise than for anything else.

Buffalo Hunter was still amazing himself with the telescope, when Ted heard Godey calling from a roof near the *placita*.

"Just a minute!" Ted yelled. He signaled the Kiowa that they had to go.

Reluctantly, Buffalo Hunter left the magic glass. He shook his head when Ted pointed across the rooftops toward the back of the fort. The Indian pulled some of the rope from the corner, motioning for Ted to let him down over the wall.

Ted tried to talk him out of the idea, but Buffalo Hunter had his mind made up. Ted let him down over the high wall and drew the rope up.

Buffalo Hunter looked up, grinned, and then set off at a trot to go around the fort and get his pony.

"Where's your friend?" Godey asked Ted later in a room on the west side.

Ted explained how Buffalo Hunter had left the fort.

One of the Frenchmen clapped his hands to his head and said, "Now all the Indians will know that they can also climb up on a rope!"

"You worry too much, Batiste," Godey said. "The Indians will never bother this place." He turned to Ted. "As long as you're here, we want you to go over to the camp and bring back something to eat."

At the camp Jackson assembled the items that Godey had requested. "It's not that they don't have food," he said, "but it's the kind what it is, not fitten for a man like Colonel Frémont to put in his stomach. Them Frenchies, they eat anything—snails, lizards, bad pork, fat dog . . ."

"I ate some dog myself," Ted said. "It wasn't too bad, except I kept thinking about it all afternoon."

Snow was falling when he returned from delivering the supplies to the fort. He went into the Indian lodge to get a cup of Jackson's coffee. Preuss, Ned Kern, and Captain Cathcart were there in the snug warmness, the latter two busy with letters, while Preuss, as usual, was making maps.

Cathcart looked up from his letter, staring toward the dry whisper of snow on the dark lodge skins. "It's like a bad day on the moor," he mused. "Have you ever seen the moors of Scotland, young McNabb?"

"No sir."

"A pity," Cathcart said, and went back to his writing.

Ted was dozing on a pile of blankets when Henry Wise came in. For two or three days Wise had been straggling behind the expedition on some business of his own, and now he had come from visiting an Indian camp. He warmed himself at the fire, admiring the lodge.

Ted started to doze again when he heard Wise say, "A batch of them young Kiowas took off on foot to make a raid against Pawnees. Think of that, striking out on the prairie in this weather when they could have stayed in a comfortable lodge."

Ted listened to the wind-driven snow scratching at the hides. Buffalo Hunter was leading those young Kiowas, he knew. Somewhere out in the storm they were moving through the gloom like drifting wolves.

For the first time Ted understood how far apart he and Buffalo Hunter were in their thinking and living. There was sadness in the thought, like the wild, lonesome call of the wolves at Chouteau's Island.

He wondered if he would ever see Buffalo Hunter again.

CHAPTER 8

Snow Bathing

FOUR INCHES OF SNOW lay on the ground the next morning. The sky was still overcast. Colonel Frémont announced that the expedition would wait another day before going on upriver. He was still trying to get more information about the mountain passes at the head of the Rio Grande del Norte River—or the Rio Grande, as it was more simply called.

Godey explained to Ted that traders like Antoine Leroux and Antoine Robidoux were familiar with all the routes between the Rio Grande and the drainage of the Colorado River. But since neither the traders nor any of their men were around now, Frémont would have to get second-hand information from men who had talked to those who knew the country at the head of the Rio Grande.

Before noon the sky cleared, and then Ted had his first good view of the mountains.

Far distant on his left were the Spanish Peaks, two white-crested cones standing strongly against the far blue sky. Off to the right and farther away loomed the great peak that Zebulon Pike had named for himself, and failed to climb. Its dark slopes led up toward gleaming white crests. The distance was so great that the mountains seemed to offer no great challenge.

"They don't look so bad," Ted said to Breckenridge, who was squatted nearby, repairing his saddle.

Breckenridge squinted across the white glare of the snow. "Not from here. You've got to get into mountains before you can understand anything about them, and then sometimes all you want to do is get out as fast as you can."

Deftly, Breckenridge cut holes in a cinch strap with a leather punch, and began to lace the strap to the ring on his saddle. "You wrote anything to your folks yet?"

"Not yet," Ted admitted.

"You'd better. This is the last place where you'll have a chance to send a letter back. From here to California there's nothing."

"I can write then. We'll be there in a few weeks, won't we?"

"I don't know." Breckenridge didn't sound very hopeful. "Everything we hear about the snow is bad."

"You're not worried, are you?"

Breckenridge hesitated. "You'd better write to your folks, bub."

Ted didn't get to the letter right away. Once more he had to take a kettle of food over to the fort. In return he brought back butter that smelled as if it had been stored in the fort since its early days. Others found it a treat, but Ted's taste was still somewhat sensitive. One bite of it was enough for him.

When the snow began to melt in the afternoon, Doc Kern heated water in a big camp kettle, grabbed a handful of soap, and took a bath. He stood in the open on an old buffalo hide, dipping a towel into the water and slopping it over his body.

Antoine watched and shuddered. "He'll die of something, doing that. Bathing is very bad in wintertime."

Ned and Dick Kern didn't think so. They began to bathe, jostling the Doctor off the hide. He retaliated by throwing handfuls of snow at them.

Preuss came stomping out of the Indian lodge and said, "This is goot!" Soon he was taking a bath, too.

Ted felt his hair. He ran his fingers along one cheek and felt the oily grime he had picked up during the last few weeks. He guessed he could stand a washing.

Soon the camp was filled with naked figures slopping water out of kettles. Now and then there were howls, when someone sneaked up behind a bather and showered him with snow.

The warm water was fine, but the wind against Ted's wet body made him break out in goose pimples. He stayed with the chore until he felt that he was reasonably clean. Later, warming by the fire with his clothes on, he began to itch all over from the strong soap he had used.

"You see?" Antoine bobbed his head knowingly. "You have destroyed your health by bathing in winter." Antoine was not about to subject himself to any such punishment. He scratched comfortably and drew his long woollen coat about him, grinning.

Under Breckenridge's direction, Ted spent most of the afternoon helping to repair pack equipment. Then he had to ride out to bring back Poche and three other mules that had run away.

Poche put up his usual protest, kicking and braying. Ted rapped him a few times with a rope, then let him have his way, just as long as the mule kept headed back to camp.

At last, Ted got around to writing his letter. Only Preuss was in Colonel Frémont's lodge. Ted borrowed writing material from him. Then he sat looking blankly at the page of paper, scratching, until Preuss stared at him and asked, "You have some little deer from the Indians, ja?"

"Little deer?"

"Louses! You have caught louses from the Indians, ja?"

"No!" Ted said indignantly. "I itch from that bath."

"So do I." Preuss scratched vigorously and resumed his work on a map.

After some time Ted began to write.

We are at Bent's Ft. Many Indians here. It snowed last night but now it is melting. I am fine. I saw the mountains today.

After that he couldn't think of anything more to say, so he sealed the letter and addressed it. "How does a letter ever get back to St. Louis, Mr. Preuss?"

"Someone always goes—traders, trappers, soldiers. Leave it and we will put it with the others."

That night, while pens were scratching at paper on the folding tables in Frémont's lodge, the Colonel wrote a letter to Senator Benton, his father-in-law.

He reported good progress so far, and commended Tom Fitzpatrick for his work with the various tribes of Indians assembled at Big Timbers. He mentioned that both Indians and whites predicted an unusually severe winter on the basis of the deep snows already in the mountains.

Colonel Frémont added that he was not discouraged, and thought that he could force his way through the snow, since his party was in good spirits and health and well supplied. With reasonable success, he said, he expected to reach California about the eighth of January.

After he finished the letter, Colonel Frémont sat staring at the hide walls. His eyes were tired. He thought of his recent court-martial in Washington. Terribly unfair, he felt. Who could blame him for resigning from the Army, where West Point officers formed a tight, selfish clique that looked down on all those who had won their way by hard work and honest success.

He studied the bearded faces around the table. These men had few worries. All the weight of this expedition was on him. He must not fail.

The Colonel rose and walked to the doorway of the lodge, looking out on the campfires. Some of the Frenchmen were singing. Looking at the cold stars reminded him that he must recheck his reading with the sextant and talk to Preuss about it.

He needed a reliable guide. He had to have a trustworthy guide before plunging into unknown mountains.

CHAPTER 9

Old Bill Williams

ON THE WAY UP the Arkansas to Fort Pueblo, the expedition kept away from the river, traveling on barren ground. In the early morning, when the earth was still frozen, the going was easy enough, but warming winds melted the crust each day, and it was then that mules slipped and bumped into each other at every steep dip they crossed.

On the left the Spanish Peaks stood clear against the sky, with other mountains coming into view behind them. The route the expedition followed was not very steep, but hour by hour they were going upward, fighting altitude as well as distance.

Some of the mules showed signs of faltering. The long plains crossing had taken much out of them, and now the effects were showing. Only six horses remained with the party, the others having been exchanged for mules.

Ranging far ahead, or out to the flanks of the expedition, the hunters found little game. Scott brought in a deer, while Martin and others shot an occasional antelope, but no buffalo were sighted.

Since leaving Bent's Fort, Godey, Ned Kern, King, and Ted had shared the same cooking mess and the same tent, with Godey doing most of the cooking.

Though some of the mules were weakening, the expedition made fair time; they had passed the mouth of the Huerfano River, and marched on to Fort Pueblo.

"That ain't much of a fort," Ted exclaimed, when he caught his first glimpse of the adobe structure across the Arkansas.

"It is only a place," Antoine said. "A roost for trappers and traders and all manner of wandering people to stay for a while in the winter. There is no trader to control the post, so it is merely some mud walls and people."

Ted had no chance to visit Fort Pueblo that day, for he was assigned guard duty as soon as the expedition went into camp on the south side of the river. The site was near a string of abandoned cottonwood log cabins called Mormontown, where two years before Mormons had started a settlement. After one winter, however, they had gone on to the Great Salt Lake Valley.

"I don't blame them," Ted said, after Breckenridge had told him the story.

When Ted went out to watch the mules, he saw two boys on foot herding cows near the river bottom. He felt superior to them, since he had one of Godey's horses. He wasn't riding it because he was giving it a chance to forage, but at least he had a mount in case any of the mules tried to stray.

He was wearing one of the pairs of moccasins Buffalo Hunter had given him. At first, they had made his feet tired, and then Antoine had explained that he must walk pigeon-toed in order to make his feet conform to the shape of the moccasins.

The deer hair Buffalo Hunter had given Ted was to put inside his moccasins when the weather was bitter, Antoine said. "And I will show you how to sew leggings to keep the snow from filling your moccasins," he promised.

Across the river, there was a loud argument going on near the fort. Men were shouting, dogs were barking, and mules were braying. Then two gunshots sounded.

None of the men loafing near some adobe houses seemed unduly excited by the uproar, so Ted guessed that nothing much had happened.

He watched a scarecrow-looking figure ride out from the fort on a brown mule. The man forded the river. He was a raw-boned old fellow with rust-colored hair stringing wild in the wind. Riding with only one foot in the stirrup, he was hunched up as if he had a pain in his stomach.

His blackened buckskin pants were slick and shiny from much wear. They struck his legs about halfway to the knee. Passing close to Ted, the rider gave the boy a squinty look. His features were sharp and weathered, with smallpox pits on cheeks and forehead.

He was mumbling to himself as he rode, a rifle in a

buckskin case across his thighs, and a knife with a rawhide wrapped handle in a case at his side. His blanket coat was ragged and flapping in the wind.

Fascinated and partly awed by the man's strange, wild appearance, Ted gulped and said, "Hello mister."

The old fellow grunted something in return, and then, still muttering to himself, rode on toward the camp.

Some old trapper who had stayed alone in the mountains for too many seasons, Ted guessed.

To Ted's surprise, Colonel Frémont rushed forward to welcome the man heartily. "Bill!" Ted heard him shout. "I was hoping we'd find you here. It's been a long time, hasn't it?"

"This child don't keep no track of time, Colonel." The man called Bill got off the mule. "I heard you was straggling up the river on another Californy trip."

"That's right! California it is."

Bill caught sight of Godey. "By old Ephraim! It's Alex! I heard you married a rich widow and settled down, hoss."

Godey slapped the old man on the back. "I tried my best, Bill, but she got away." He grinned. "Where you been cached?"

Bill waved one long arm vaguely toward the west. "Here and about." His voice was querulous. "Beaver's scarce. Trading's worse. The whole country is going to pieces."

"It's not quite that bad," Frémont said. "Come in the lodge, Bill. I want to talk to you."

Frémont and Bill, followed by Godey and King, went

into the lodge. Soon afterward Haler joined them. If anything was happening around camp, Haler always liked to be in on it, Ted knew.

Whatever they were discussing took a long time. Men approached the lodge door and were turned away. Now and then, Ted could hear Bill's voice raised in high-pitched talk, as if he were complaining about something.

When the visitor at last came out of the lodge, Colonel Frémont walked over to the brown mule with him, and stood there for several minutes talking. Then the old fellow started back toward the fort.

For the second time he passed close to where Ted was standing. Once more he stared at him from rheumy eyes set in a sharp-nosed face.

"Hello!" Ted said, but Bill rode on without answering.

Not long afterward, Ned Kern came out to relieve Ted so he could eat supper.

"Who was that old coot?" Ted asked.

"That would take a heap of telling. It's Old Bill Williams, if you want just a name."

"Who's he to make such a fuss over?"

"Well to start, he's a Mountain Man who's been around since the rivers were dug and the dirt thrown up to make the peaks. They say there's no one who knows the part of the mountains where we're going like Old Bill."

"Is he crazy?"

Kern laughed. "He acts a mite queer, yes, but he's not cracked. Some of his oddness, I suppose, comes from staying so long by himself on trapping trips. He doesn't asso-

ciate much with other trappers, though he lives with Indians a lot of the time, your uncle says."

"I suppose he wants to go with us," Ted said. "An
old fellow like that probably would play out the first
week."

"I don't know how bad Old Bill wants to go," Kern
said, "but I *can* say that the Colonel wants him to go awful
bad. That's why he talked Old Bill into guiding us."

"Him!" Ted looked toward the mud fort. "Why, he
must be eighty years old!"

"More like seventy, I'd say. But don't worry about
Old Bill holding together. He's nothing but rawhide and
wire. He'll be waiting for the rest of us to catch up most of
the time."

"What did he think about all the snow stories we've
been hearing?"

Kern nodded slowly. "He says they're true, but he
thinks we can get through. Now go eat, and tell Haler to
send the next guard out as soon as he can. I'm hungry, too."

As soon as he got to camp Ted heard plenty of talk
about Old Bill Williams. Bill had guided Colonel Frémont
once before. He was one of the best rifle shots in the mountains. Godey said there was no doubt that he knew all the
passes at the head of the Rio Grande.

Ted guessed that everything they were saying was
true, but he still wondered how an old coot like Bill Williams could stand up to a hard trip through snowy mountains.

After eating, Ted walked a short distance from the
camp to study the mountains. They looked much closer

now, though he realized that they were still many miles away.

Dusk approached. On the high snowy crests the light was still shining. As it faded, the snow took on a faint blue color. Ted wondered how cold it was up there.

In the morning the expedition forded the river. The Arkansas was strong flowing, edged with ice. When water slopped up in Ted's moccasins, he learned how cold it felt.

At closer view the fort was even less imposing than from a distance. Scattered near it were little adobe huts and brush shelters, with here and there a weed-choked patch where someone had tried to raise a garden.

The inhabitants of the huts and the men who straggled from the fort to look at the pack train were the most villainous looking people Ted had ever seen—bedraggled Indians, half breeds, hairy trappers in worn buckskins, white traders, and Mexicans, some with huge rings in their ears.

It wouldn't do to wear those rings in a fight with St. Louis rivermen, Ted thought; they'd make a convenient handle to pull off an ear.

Not far from the fort the expedition halted, while Colonel Frémont, Ned Kern, and a few others went inside.

Old Bill Williams returned with them. Behind his saddle he had a small pack. He was wearing a blanket cap with two of its folds laced with rawhide and sticking up like the ears of a wolf.

"Let's go to Californy, Colonel," he said, and rode off at the head of the expedition, not even looking back to see if the others were going to follow.

"What's it like inside the fort?" Ted asked Ned Kern.

Kern made a face. "Horses and mules and chickens and men all mixed up in one bad smell. I wouldn't winter there for all the tea in China."

"This is the last fort we'll see, huh?"

"If you can call that mud mess a fort. We'll stop at a little settlement where we've arranged to buy corn; and after that, you won't see anything but Indian lodges between there and California."

The date was November 22, 1848. The fourth expedition was starting its second month of travel.

The approach to the mountains was so gradual that it was hard to believe the expedition had climbed more than the five thousand feet showing on Colonel Frémont's barometer. Now and then gulches and deep washes broke across the rolling land.

It was a warm day, with the snow underfoot melting rapidly. The long run of red hills that led toward Pikes Peak, on the right, was closing in rapidly, and the mountains on the left were crowding to form a solid line.

"Where do we turn into the mountains?" Ted asked Antoine.

"Not far now."

Ted saw Antoine studying the snowy peaks quietly.

"What's it like up there?"

"You will see."

They camped that night in a bottom near the river, with good forage for the mules and plentiful firewood. A snowstorm was obscuring the mountains to the north, but

it was still mild where they were. Then there came a light
rain, that passed as quickly as a summer shower.

When they were ready to move in the morning, Old
Bill was already across the river waiting.

"This is the last of the Arkansas," Ned Kern said. "Between here and California we'll have to cross other rivers,
but we'll never have another friendly one like this to follow for so many miles."

Captain Cathcart crossed with Ted. He wiped his
mustache with his hand. "So we've crossed the Rubicon,
eh?" He smiled as he looked up toward the sharp-spined
Sangre de Cristo Range. "Now if we only had some of
Hannibal's elephants, eh men?"

The Start

HARDSCRABBLE WAS A LITTLE adobe settlement in a warm valley, surrounded by junipers, pines, and scrub oaks. Here, old Mountain Men often wintered. A few of them had taken permanent roots, with Mexican employees and Indian wives to cultivate corn and squash in the fields along the creek.

Strings of red peppers, the traditional Mexican welcoming sign, hung at some of the doorways. Numerous corn cribs were built close to the houses.

Three bearded old mountaineers yelled at Bill when he rode in at the head of the expedition. In his high, whiney voice he exchanged pleasantries with them. He got off his mule and went into one of the houses, not appearing again until long after camp was made.

That was Old Bill Williams for you; camp chores never bothered him. He was the guide and that was all he did. His presence with the expedition, Ted had observed, seemed to make everyone confident. No one had to worry about floundering around lost somewhere in the mountains, as long as Old Bill was along.

They stayed two nights at Hardscrabble. At first, Ted thought he would have a chance to go hunting, but for two days all he did was shell corn. Almost everyone else was busy at the same task, shaving the red kernels from the cob onto hides spread on the ground.

Others were busy making canvas sacks to carry the corn. Colonel Frémont had bought about 130 bushels to feed the mules during the time when they would be in the high country, where all forage would be buried under snow.

Godey traded the last of the horses for mules. Off and on he had ridden Dick, a strong, nimble little mule; from now on it would be mules for everyone, with the life and success of the expedition depending almost entirely on how well the animals held up.

In spite of the corn shelling and other chores, including a careful inspection of all saddles and gear, as well as re-shoeing some of the mules, the stay at Hardscrabble was a pleasant interlude for Ted.

Again, the expedition was warned about snow in the mountains. "Turrible," one of the residents said. "Snow's neck-deep on a tall Indian all the way to the Grand."

"How do you know?" Colonel Frémont asked the man.

"Seed some Utes three, four weeks back on their way to Manitou Springs. Said they'd lost half their ponies in the mountains."

The men of the expedition had heard dire tales of bad
weather so many times that they discounted this latest
warning. Theirs was a strong party, well organized, led by
the greatest Western explorer of the time, guided by a veteran who certainly was not going to get them into any impossible fix.

Ted was ready and eager to go on. "Now we'll tackle
the Sangre de Cristo, huh?" he asked his uncle.

"Soon enough," Godey answered. "First, we have
some little hills to cross before we reach the Sangre
de Cristo."

Even the riding animals were laden with corn when
the expedition left Hardscrabble. Shambling along in a
wobbly walk that took him from side to side, Old Bill led
the way as if he were crossing his own back yard.

Godey's "little hills" turned out to be the Wet Mountains. There was no trail and the way was narrow and winding much of the time. On the ridges the snow had melted
or been blown away, but it lay heavy and wet in the hollows and on the slopes that faced north, and that was
where the going was slow and slippery.

Colonel Frémont, Godey, and King went on ahead,
breaking trail where Old Bill led them. Colonel Frémont
was up early and stayed up late, taking barometric read-
ings, conferring with Preuss about the route maps, and
making notes of his own.

One night, while camped in three feet of snow on a
hillside, the party listened to the Colonel compliment
them for their efforts so far. "A railroad would have little

difficulty passing through here," he said, "though it would not be along the exact route we have followed.

"Nor do I anticipate any great problems crossing the Sangre de Cristo at Robidoux Pass, and I know that the valley beyond will offer no obstacles. Once we've crossed at the head of the Rio Grande to the Colorado drainage, the problems of game and forage will be materially lessened. . . ." His dark eyes glowing in the firelight, Colonel Frémont went on. "I know that none of us expects a journey of ease and comfort, but we are not facing an impossible task, and there will be rewards when we have accomplished our purpose."

Firelight fell on the bearded faces of men listening to the Colonel's words. They believed. Haler nodded his head wisely. It was hard for Ted McNabb to picture a railroad running through the snow-clogged canyon below, but he, too, believed Colonel Frémont.

There was something about the man that gave Ted confidence, he wanted to go along with Frémont where he said he would go, if only to have a small share in the great things Frémont would do.

Down among the trees the mules were pawing at the snow, nibbling at the tree limbs. Now and then one of them brayed a hungry protest. The corn was only an emergency ration to carry them through the worst of the high country. They would be hungry until the expedition broke completely out of the snow.

While Colonel Frémont went back to his tent to work, Ted resumed sewing smoked-hide leggings onto his moccasins. In dry snow the moccasins did not soak through. In wet snow they turned soggy soon enough, but it was simple to dry them out at night.

Men who were wearing heavy boots were having more difficulty. The leather dried out stiff and came apart at the cobbling. Already several of the party had tried to trade Ted out of his extra pairs of moccasins.

"No, no," Antoine said. "Do not trade. You will need all your moccasins. Others can make their own."

Slowly, fighting snow and rocks, the expedition pushed its way out of the narrow passages into a widening valley that carried them up toward the top of the Wet Mountains. Now the sharp crests of the Sangre de Cristo came into full view.

That harsh range was called by various names: the Taos Mountains, the Sierra Blanca, or, in English, the White Mountains; but long before, the Spanish had named it well—because of the crimson sunsets that often lay along its peaks—as Sangre de Cristo, Blood of Christ.

Miles ahead, beyond the pitching hills still to be crossed and up the valley white with snow, lay a gap that Old Bill Williams pointed out—Robidoux Pass.

Antoine and Ted squinted toward the distant notch. "Robidoux took carts and wagons through that," Antoine said. "Many years ago he made the road."

"He went through there in winter?"

"No, not in winter."

Bucking up and down the hills was wearisome. Often there were warm little valleys with signs of game, but the expedition could not tarry. Every night mules strayed. The

whole expedition could not be delayed to hunt for them,
so some of the packs would be left behind while the train
went on, with a few men detailed to round up the strays,
pack them, and catch up.

Haler always volunteered for this extra work. It was a
job that had to be done, but Haler gave the impression
that he wanted special credit for his labors.

With most of the expedition still walking, they went
up the Wet Mountain Valley. Here the snow was slush.
It soaked quickly through boots and moccasins. Almost
everyone was wearing leather leggings tied on with rawhide.

"I don't see how Old Bill gets along, bare-legged that
way," Ted said to Ned Kern one day. Kern was sitting on a
log during the noon rest, sketching a view of the pass
ahead.

"He's part Indian. Besides, he rides most of the time,
so he doesn't get as wet as the rest of us. He'd wear wool,
if he had any, but I think Old Bill has been having bad
times ever since that spree in Taos last spring."

"What was that?"

"Didn't Godey tell you?"

"No."

"Well, it seems that Old Bill took a batch of furs with
him. He'd been wintering with some Utes and he promised
to sell their furs for them. He sold the pelts and then he
went on a big drunk with the money.

"Then sometime last summer he led soldiers against
a bunch of raiding Apaches, and it turned out that some
Utes were with the Apaches. I guess the Indians took a bad

mauling. Old Bill got his arm broke with a rifle shot. Now his own people, the Utes, are mad at him. I hope we don't meet any of them on this trip."

Ted looked at Old Bill hunched over a tiny fire, chewing on a piece of deer meat.

"He really is part Ute?"

"No," Kern said. "What I meant is that he's lived with Indians so long, he's taken on their habits and thinking."

"Catch up, catch up!" Godey shouted, and the cry was carried through the camp.

Weary men rose, checked the mule packs, and once more resumed the slippery way toward the pass. If there was a road, Ted thought, they surely weren't following it.

Sometimes there was bare ground with grass. Then the mules would try to break out of line to forage. It was always a chore to get them moving again.

Every day the hunters searched hard for game, but it was scarce. The few deer they brought in were quickly consumed; Old Bill and some of the others ate the livers raw.

In a little park under the pass they saw the first marks of Robidoux's road. It wasn't much, but it was reassuring to know that someone had once driven wagons this way.

That night, wind came blasting from the heights, bearing frightful cold with it. In spite of snow, it had not been very cold before. Few of the light tents had been used at night. Now the cold was numbing, and the wind so strong that the linen tents blew down as fast as men put them up.

The mules turned their rumps to the wind and stood

with lowered heads. Men's hats went flying into the trees. The edges of canvas on the packs lifted and fell, snapping like pistol shots.

Ted knew he could sleep in Frémont's lodge, but he chose to stay outside. He helped King and McGehee build a windbreak of trees and logs.

"Why don't you stay in the lodge?" King asked.

"Too smoky. Besides, Preuss and Creutzfeldt snore."

King laughed. "You'll do, boy."

The windbreak was fine when the wind held steadily off the pass, but there were times when it swirled in the wrong direction, straight across the fire, flattening the flames into gusty tongues that licked at the clothing of anyone standing close.

Hovering over the fire, McGehee suddenly found his pants legs smoldering as the wind veered. He leaped away to kneel in the snow. "We'll have to take turns sleeping or we'll wake up looking like roasted pigs."

"I could use a roast pig right now," King said.

Ted took the first watch. He kept the fire going and watched for burning embers on the blankets of the sleepers. A dozen times he had to rub out fire spots in the wool.

McGehee and King didn't get much rest.

Ted thought he wouldn't be able to sleep a wink. When his turn came, he wrapped up in the blankets, pulled his hat tight around his ears, and prepared for a bad night. He heard McGehee say, "I used to complain about the heat in Mississippi."

That was the last Ted knew, until King woke him just before daylight. Tired men with soot-smudged faces and blankets around their shoulders were huddled at the fires. Some of the mules, including Poche, had crowded in close to share the warmth, while others were still standing among the trees, their rumps plastered white with snow.

The wind was still bellowing.

After a hasty breakfast, the expedition started into Robidoux Pass.

CHAPTER 11

Robidoux Pass

Now IT WAS SNOWING. Eyes streamed, noses ran, and flesh across cheeks and foreheads was so stiff that any movement made one think the skin was cracking.

Robidoux's road was of no help, for it held more drifted snow than the hills above or below it. The expedition broke into small groups, each trying to find the best passage through the notch.

Bare spots afforded easier footing, but they were few and far between. In the trees and willows along the plunging creek that gurgled under the ice, the snow was always soft and deep.

While the pass itself was not extremely steep, nor the snow impassable, wind was an enemy that made the climb miserable. It tore the breath from men's mouths and laid a stinging whip of snow crystals across their faces.

Although the mules went into the blast with steady patience, they turned their backs to it at every stop. Some of them got their chance to break away just after topping a high ridge.

Doc Kern's tall wool hat blew off. He plunged after it, only to have it skip out of his reach each time it was almost within his grasp. When he did catch it at last, he threw his rifle down on the hat. "There! That'll hold you!"

McGehee and the other Kerns were laughing. They relaxed their vigilance for a moment, and that was enough for four of the mules to break away. In minutes they lost the labor of an hour's climb. The men who went after them—the Kerns, McGehee, and Proue—dragged wearily into camp late that afternoon.

It was still snowing in gusts, with the wind bitter. The only fuel available was willows, which men piled high on the crackling fires. The mules came crowding in to get warm—trembling, gaunt, with icicles hanging from their lips and nostrils, their breath smoking white.

"Some of the animals, I think, do not get over the pass tomorrow," Antoine predicted gloomily.

He underestimated the mules. Tired and hungry as they were, they wanted to cross the pass and get away from the brutal wind.

After a late start the next morning, the pack animals bucked into the pass with a will. It was still storming. At one point, while resting in the lee of pines under a rocky ridge, Old Bill encouraged the party by saying, "Two trappers I knowed well froze solid here last winter. Buried them right about there, we did." He pointed toward a snowbank.

McGehee, always quiet spoken, shook his head and said, "Cheerful old fellow, isn't he?"

The stout Preuss, his face gleaming red with cold, grunted, "Vell, I don't freeze here, I bet!" He went tramping up the trail, carrying the leather map case which he would not have packed on any mule.

By noon the expedition had topped the pass. The winding descent was steeper than the ascent of the eastern side. They encountered the debris of a snowslide from the spring before. Aspen trees had been swept across the road in a fierce tangle. Now the trees were under the snow—crisscrossed, stacked, splintered.

In the lead with Old Bill, Colonel Frémont called for axes. Ted was one of those who went forward to pull the trees from the snow after others had chopped them. In places the tangle was five feet deep, but the expedition hacked a way through and went on without too great a loss of time.

Not long afterward Ted had his first full view of the San Luis Valley, a vast snow-covered park that ran for fifty miles westward toward shining mountains. On the north, more mountains enclosed it.

Antoine pointed south. "Down there is Taos. Down there it is pleasant in winter."

Huge sand dunes lay below, at the very foot of the pass, their tops brown, their hollows white with snow. From there Ted's eyes followed the long, treeless expanse that led to the distant mountains. At least there would be no more climbing for a while.

They camped in a hollow of juniper and cottonwood.

Those who had not already replaced their rotting boots with moccasins were busy making new footgear.

That night, December 3, 1848, a howling wind piled snow on blankets and tents.

The expedition spent three days near the sand dunes, skirting the northern edge of the tremendous brown hills. The hoofs of the mules sank deep into the sand, but the wind quickly covered all marks of passage. On the crested ridges of the dunes the wind made weird, whining music.

A driving snowstorm on the third day forced the expedition back to their camp of the previous night, after they had gone less than two miles. Warming in Frémont's lodge, Ted heard the Colonel say, "I'm not satisfied with this side of Robidoux, Bill. I think we'd better examine your pass."

At ease on a buffalo robe, Old Bill rubbed his sleeve across his sharp nose. "You're welcome, Colonel."

Godey was in charge of the main expedition that day, while Frémont took a small group with Old Bill to look at Williams Pass, a notch in the mountains that was plainly visible from the valley floor.

"That's the trouble with expeditions," Doc Kern said, watching the surveyors ride away. "Somebody always wants to explore something when your tail end is freezing."

"That's why we're here," Ned Kern said.

McGehee was trying a woollen scarf around his ears. "Old Bill claims that pass himself. It's named after him."

Ducatel's mustache was white with frost. He looked up at the Sangre de Cristo and said, "He can have it."

Struggling through the soft sand at the edge of the dunes, the expedition fought a freezing wind that whipped the breath of the mules back against their chests until the front of the animals was white with ice.

At noon the thermometer was below zero, and it was even colder when they camped that afternoon in the last grove of cottonwoods at the edge of the treeless valley.

Colonel Frémont came in late with his party. King's feet were almost frozen. Even Preuss admitted that it had been a miserable day for surveying.

"You'll sleep in the lodge tonight," Godey told Ted. "No matter how tough you think you are, you're coming inside."

From then on Ted was a member of the group that shared the lodge with Frémont.

While they were packing in the morning, Colonel Frémont walked about briskly among the men. "We've done well in crossing the Sangre de Cristo in two days. Day after tomorrow we'll reach the Rio Grande Del Norte, where we'll find plenty of timber.

"We also will have a good chance for game, Old Bill says. Our supplies are holding up well, and we still have more than enough corn to carry the mules across the San Juans. Once we get out of the snow and into grass again, the mules can forage for themselves."

"Mules," Dick Kern grumbled to his brother Ned. "I've had enough of mules to last me two lifetimes."

The expedition started into the valley. Within a short distance they encountered a frozen marsh, where the hoofs of the mules plopped through the crust to make little pot-holes from which a steamy vapor rose.

, Frost crystals hung in the air in a glittering haze. The mountains ahead were obscured by a storm. Looking back, Ted saw a leaden cloud hanging low over the dunes, while on the white wedges of the Sangre de Cristo the wind was whipping long streamers of snow.

The mules crunched steadily into the valley.

Some of the men were riding now. Ducatel was one of them. Before noon he almost froze to death in the saddle. Breckenridge and Wise helped him down and made him walk to restore his circulation.

They covered twenty-two miles that day. When it was time to camp, they were in the middle of a waste of snow and sage.

Colonel Frémont ordered double corn rations for the mules. That some of the animals had lasted this far was a wonder to Ted. Poche was one of the strongest. Like all the others, he was thinned down to bones under his thick winter coat of hair, but he was still able to bear his pack easily.

Fires sprang up quickly. The sage and rabbit brush burned so fast that men kept warm just chopping fuel. Old Bill disdained the larger blazes, and especially the work required to keep them going. He hunched over his own tiny fire, feeding a few small sticks into it.

"Meat," he grumbled. "That's what this coon needs, ye hear?"

The men of the expedition were used to Old Bill's mumbling and scarcely paid any attention to it. Ted was still awed by the Mountain Man and his strange ways, and the fact that he had crossed the Sangre de Cristo wearing less clothing than anyone else, without appearing to have suffered. He screwed his courage up and went over to Old Bill.

"Do you think we'll find game on the Rio Grande, Mr. Williams?"

Old Bill turned his bleary gaze on the boy. "I find game anywhere!" he snorted.

"I mean enough for all of us."

The guide stared into the flames for a while. "I've seed bufflers by the hundreds bellowing and stomping on their way through Cochetopy Pass. Mountain bufflers, big and dark."

"Do you think we'll find any?"

Old Bill acted as if he hadn't heard the question. When he spoke, he was musing to himself. "Gone under. Gone."

Ted backed away. He figured Old Bill wasn't altogether crazy, but he sure was queer.

A creaking cold came down on the exposed camp. The Sangre de Cristo turned from shining white to dusky blue. The hobbled mules hopped about, browsing on the sage. The guards stamped their feet and flailed their arms against their bodies to keep warm.

Ted wondered how the fires would look from the mountains they had crossed. From up there, probably, you couldn't even see them, or if you could, they would be no more than specks of light flickering in a vast loneliness.

It was snowing when Ted went to sleep.

At times during the night he heard men cutting sage

for the fires. And he heard the blanketed mules shaking
their heads vigorously, clacking their long ears together to
keep them from freezing.

Sometime in the dead of night a man shouted an
alarm.

Godey reacted instantly. He was out of bed with his
rifle in his hands before Ted was fully awake.

"Some of the mules are gone!"

Frémont was up by then and soon the whole camp
was stirring. Ted started to rise, and discovered four inches
of snow on top of his bed. He lay down again.

Some of the guards had stayed too long at the fires,
allowing about half of the mules to drift away. "They go
back to the Sangre de Cristo, I think," Proue said.

His surmise was right, for when Godey and others
went out in the storm to study the tracks of the runaways,
they discovered that the mules had gone back toward the
mountains.

It was about three o'clock in the morning.

Proue, Breckenridge, and of course Haler, along with
others, went after the mules, returning with them shortly
before daylight.

No one rested much after the alarm was given.

Through another day of intermittent snow and cold
and haze that hung like fog, the expedition marched on.
They came that afternoon to a long grove of cottonwood
trees not far from the Rio Grande River.

"Good fires tonight!" Antoine said happily.

The men dug down through two feet of snow to set
up camp. Poche and some of the other mules hung close

to the shovelers, and ate the grass as soon as it was exposed. Later, Ted cut tree limbs and stripped the bark to feed Poche, Ney, Scrap, and Godey's riding mule, Dick. He blanketed them carefully and sneaked them an extra ration of corn.

Chopping fuel in the cold dusk, Ted paused to look up the river. Low-reaching hills were beginning to crowd the stream from both sides, forming a channel that pointed toward the dimly seen summits of the San Juans.

Ted wondered how the next passage through the mountains would compare to Robidoux's old road over the Sangre de Cristo.

CHAPTER 12

The Decision

TED LAY ON HIS blankets against the back wall of the lodge
and listened to Colonel Frémont trying to pin Old Bill
down to details on the crossings in the San Juans.

Old Bill spat at the fire. "Ain't much to tell, Colonel.
In a regular winter Carnero and Cochetopy is easy. Sum-
mertime, wagons been . . ."

Frémont shook his head. "We've passed the entrance
to the Cochetopa already. It's too far north, as I've said."

Godey was sitting cross-legged at the fire. His black
beard was bushy and ragged. "The Colonel wants to follow
a straight line as close as possible, Bill."

The guide grunted. "No mountains was ever made for
straight line going, ye hear?"

"I think I fully realize that fact." Frémont said.

"Never seed a worse winter," Old Bill grunted.

Captain Cathcart was listening intently. At the folding table, Preuss paused in his work to light his pipe. He stared with an expression of annoyance at Old Bill. Back in the shadows, Jackson was sitting on a case, his eyes frightened as he looked from one man to another.

Henry King was sitting closer to the fire. His face was tired and haggard.

"You think we can get through Del Norte Pass, Williams Pass—whatever you want to call it?" Godey asked.

Old Bill hesitated, studying the flames. "Snow's bad. Worse'n I thought. You're going to lose a heap of them mules, Colonel."

"That's part of the risk," Colonel Frémont said briskly. "What I want to know is your opinion of the chances."

"Told you once," Old Bill grumbled.

"That was before we came this far." Frémont glanced at Godey for an instant.

Old Bill pursed his lips. "You want to go to Californy, I'll tell you. Head down the Rio Grande toward Taos."

Colonel Frémont sighed. "You don't seem to understand. This expedition is going west as close to the 38th parallel as the terrain will permit. That much is settled. What we face now is the selection of a pass."

Old Bill shook his head. "Them mountains don't care much about your 38th thing, Colonel. When we come down off Robidoux's Pass, I said Cochetopy, remember?"

"The Cochetopa is too far north," Frémont explained patiently. "What about Carnero Pass?"

"They used to come by the hundreds through the

Cochetopy," Old Bill said. "Bufflers. Wagh! Fat cows, old bulls a-stomping. Gone. All gone."

Ted had heard that before. He raised up higher on his elbow to have a better look at Old Bill. The others exchanged quiet looks. A twig in the small fire popped. Smoke spiraled lazily toward the apex of the lodge.

"Carnero Pass?" Frémont asked.

"I know it, I know it," Old Bill said impatiently. "It's quicker going up to my pass."

"That's what I wanted to know, and I want your opinion of the time involved in getting through."

Old Bill considered the question for a long time. "Depends on the snow. I told you in Pueblo."

Godey said quietly, "Have you gone through there in a bad winter, Bill?"

The guide shook his head.

"Are you afraid to try it?" Frémont asked gently.

That brought Old Bill's hunched shoulders up with a quick jerk. He stared hard at the Colonel. "I ain't afeerd of nothing that ever fell on the mountains or growed there or walked there on two legs or four, ye hear?"

"Then you think we can get through your pass?"

Old Bill rose and glared around the lodge. "I can go where I want to go. If your greenhorns and mules can follow me is something else."

Colonel Frémont said quietly, "I have confidence in my men and equipment. You show us the pass, and leave the rest to me."

"I'll show you a pass!" Old Bill shouted in his high voice. He went stomping out of the lodge.

Cathcart was the first to break the silence. "Unusual fellow. Touchy, eh?"

"He had to be challenged," Frémont said.

King was staring morosely at the ground. "I wonder if it was wise to bait him into it?"

Smiling, Colonel Frémont walked over to King and put a hand on his shoulder. "Don't tell me, Henry, of all my men, you're entertaining doubts that we'll push through."

"I'm here," King said. He raised his head to look at Frémont gravely. "The mules are in poor condition. We've used more corn than we figured."

The Colonel nodded. "I realize that, but we still have enough to carry them through. Once across the San Juans, each day will bring us closer to getting out of the snow. Why, I've seen it in the Sierra Nevada when I fought through ten feet of snow, and then looked down on green valleys lying under a warm sun.

"This isn't the first time that harbingers of disaster have nipped at my plans. Old Bill is cautious, yes, and perhaps we've already encountered more snow than he thought we would find, but he wouldn't have come this far if he were certain that we couldn't push over the mountains. I know Old Bill. He's independent. If he thought we couldn't cross the San Juan, he'd head that brown mule toward Taos."

Godey nodded. "He knows these mountains as no man does, and it is all the better that he is a little doubtful. If he says he will go, angry or not, we must trust him."

From the shadows Ted watched King's face. He saw

him nod slowly, but his expression was still not cheerful.

Colonel Frémont clapped King on the shoulder reassuringly, and then turned quickly to the table when Preuss asked a question about an elevation on Robidoux Pass.

For all of the concern Preuss had shown during the discussion, the country ahead might be level, with grass and game abounding. Ted rolled over on his back, watching the smoke swirl upward. He guessed that Old Bill, in spite of his snarling and whining, knew what he was doing.

Why, he had two passes named after him: the one there in the Sangre de Cristo, close to where the expedition had crossed, and the one somewhere ahead in the San Juans. It was a big thing to have something named after you. Ted knew that Colonel Frémont was given to naming rivers and peaks in honor of members of his expeditions. Mount McNabb. That had a fine sound. Ted fell asleep thinking of a snow-crowned mountain of the Rockies bearing his name.

They were all asleep in the lodge before Frémont found time to rest. He inspected the camp. For the first time in three nights, no one but the mule guards was up. The big fires that Antoine and the other Frenchmen had built were heaps of glowing embers.

Frémont warmed briefly at one, looking at the sleeping men. The more experienced members of the party had not tried to shovel the snow away from their sleeping places, but were resting on it, sandwiched in their blankets between India rubber sheets.

Gallant men, the leader thought warmly. No hardship would stop them. They had caught the spirit of the important task that faced the expedition. They would not fail.

He looked toward the mules, dark bulked in their blankets. King was right about the shortage of rations for the animals, but the problem was not critical yet. There was enough corn for ten days, and after that, conditions would improve. It was easy for even experienced men like King to underestimate the incredible spirit and endurance of mules.

The snow creaked under Frémont's moccasins as he walked back toward the lodge. Old Bill's attitude toward the next step of the journey had been growing increasingly discouraging.

A doubt touched Frémont's mind. He rejected it instantly. He could not even consider failure. At any cost, the expedition must succeed.

He looked at the sky. The air was filled with crackling cold. Overcast hid the stars. No observations tonight. Surely the weather would change soon.

Inside the lodge, he looked at the slumbering forms of weary men. Godey's young nephew, his beardless face partly covered with a blanket, was sleeping like a child. He had done well, that lad, performing a man's work without complaint.

Frémont smiled. That evening, young McNabb had asked hesitantly if he could buy one of the mules after the expedition reached California. He wanted Poche—the French word for pocket—how in the world had the boy selected that name for a mule?

"Buy him? I should say not, but he will be yours as a present when we reach California!" Frémont had said.

For so small a gesture, an impulse that he could not have resisted anyway, Frémont knew by the boy's surprised look and happy grin that he had won another convert. Great friends, great enemies. He knew well how easily he could attract both.

Restless in his energy, even when it was time to rest, he stepped over the legs of sleeping men and went to bed.

Now it was December 9, 1848. The expedition turned upriver into the narrowing gap of the Rio Grande, moving through a cold fog that hung sullenly above the frosty willows and cottonwoods. It was an oddly hushed day, with a misty unrealness clinging to the gloom. The figures of men and mules seemed ghostly, floating in the murk. For a long time no one talked loudly, even when urging the mules on.

Ted watched the dainty dip and rise of the hoofs. The queer light made blue hollows of the holes where the animals' legs punched down into the snow. And then he saw crimson splotching, where blood had spattered from legs cut by the crusted snow.

They came to a rocky point that blocked the way along the north bank of the river. Old Bill led his mule across the frozen stream and disappeared into the willows. The first pack animal that minced out on the ice slipped and fell on its side.

Grumbling packers unloaded it and helped it rise, and

the mule knocked two of them down as it scrambled back to safe footing on the near bank. The rest of the mules began to bray their fear and displeasure of the ice, when men tried to lead them across the river.

They milled and broke away, some falling, others crashing back into the animals behind them. Tempers flared. The quiet of the day was broken by the yelling of the packers.

"Wait, wait!" Proue shouted. "Dese mules, she no fool, you bet. Dey know what is no good." He took a shovel from one of the packs, dug down to the leaf mat in the willows, and began to throw the leaves on the ice.

Some of the other packers helped him, throwing chunks of frozen leaves and mold on the surface of the ice to make what seemed to be a trail across the river. Though the passage was still slippery, as Ted discovered when he jammed his heel down to break up a mass of leaves and fell on his rear, the mules accepted what appeared to be good footing.

After the first few teetered across gingerly, the rest were willing to follow; and even though several of the animals fell, those behind were no longer afraid of the ice.

Antoine wagged a finger at Ted. "What they do not know, they fear. They are sensible. They do not kill themselves to be brave." And then he looked upriver to the mountains.

Ted grinned. "You mean we're likely to kill ourselves up there by trying to be brave?"

"No, no! Do not say such things!"

"You're getting to be like Old Bill, Antoine."

When anyone even hinted of bad luck around Old Bill, the guide would protest loudly and say that bad things always happened when people talked about them beforehand. That was part of what Ned Kern had meant, when he said Old Bill thought like an Indian.

Elk tracks showed in the snow among the willows on the south bank of the Rio Grande, their trails wandering on toward the hills. Ted had never seen an elk, but he had heard that they were tremendous animals.

That night in camp Godey said, "Since you missed your buffalo, I'll take you with me in the morning when we go after elk." And then he warned, "No shooting until I say so."

"I'll remember."

They started soon after daylight. The air was sharp with frost. The hoofs of the mules made crunching sounds in the snow. Scott, Martin, Josiah Ferguson, and the Tulare Indians went along, following a well-beaten elk trail toward a grove of cottonwoods downriver.

A half-mile from the trees, the hunters, separated, some of them fanning wide to cover the sides of the grove and the far end, while Joaquin went on downriver to turn back and ride through the trees.

Godey and Ted were to cover the upper end of the grove, in case any game broke out that way. Since the other hunters had to ride farther, Ted and his uncle dismounted, waiting for their companions to get in position.

Standing still in the bitter cold wasn't pleasant, but

the thought of getting a shot at an elk kept Ted on edge.

"Remember, no quick shooting," Godey said.

Ted nodded, shivering. He could feel the coldness of his rifle through his mittens.

When Godey saw the flankers turn and ride in toward the grove, he and Ted closed in from their position.

The huge animals that burst from the trees caught Ted completely by surprise. There were six of them, tall, high-shouldered. They ran with long strides, kicking plumes from the snow, churning toward the hills on a course that would take them between Scott and Martin.

Scott's rifle boomed. Ted saw one of the elk stumble, but it caught its stride again and went surging on. Then two of the elk veered away from the herd and ran toward Ted and Godey.

Ted's mouth was dry as he watched the monstrous, ungainly creatures plough through the snow. Compared to them, the biggest deer he had ever seen was a dainty thing.

He didn't think of shooting until after he heard Godey's rifle crash. The leading elk went down, exploding snow in a white burst. The second animal turned back toward the grove, then changed its mind and ran toward the river.

Ted knelt and fired, but he was still an instant behind Godey's second shot. The running elk plunged to its knees. It staggered up and wobbled on, as Ted tried to hurry his reloading.

Gregorio's rifle sounded. The elk collapsed.

Ted started to run forward. "We got him!"

"Stay here," Godey said. "Reload your rifle, then bring the horses. I will go to make sure the elk is dead."

While he was recharging his rifle, Ted saw that Scott and Martin were already butchering the first elk Godey had killed. By the time Ted got to where Godey was working, his uncle had removed the entrails and stomach of the animal and the insides lay in a steaming mass on the snow.

"What a big one!" Ted exclaimed.

Godey offered him a slice of liver, hot and smoking. "Ugh!"

"Eat it! It will keep you from losing your teeth and growing so weak you will have to crawl before we reach California."

Ted chewed gingerly on the meat.

"Here." Godey sprinkled a pinch of gunpowder on the liver. "This is better than salt to flavor it."

Ted ate some of it. He noticed that Gregorio and Joaquin, who arrived a few minutes later, had no trouble eating the hot liver as readily as if it had been fresh, warm bread with butter on it.

Butchering the elk was a chore. Blood froze on hands as soon as they were out of the carcass. Washing them in snow made them all the colder.

When the meat of the two animals was packed on the groaning mules, the hunters puzzled Ted by going into the cottonwoods instead of back to camp. They put aside the choicest portions of the meat and began to hang the rest high in the cottonwoods.

"We can't take it all," Godey explained. "The mules

already have too much to carry through the mountains."

Ted was still puzzled. "We won't be back. Why are you bothering even to hang it up?"

"It isn't good to waste meat," Godey said.

"But we're not coming back, so . . ."

"It is never good to waste meat!"

The answer was still not clear to Ted, but it did not disturb him as it did Antoine, when he told the old Frenchman about the meat cache on returning to camp.

"Ah! Someone thinks we will not get over the mountains. It is wise to leave a cache to return to if we fail to . . ."

"That's nonsense!" Haler said. He was always overhearing remarks meant for someone else. "Of course Colonel Frémont will take us through the mountains. What's the matter, old man, are your feet cold already?"

Antoine swung around angrily. He said in French, "I have seen frozen mountains before you were born, rooster that crows all the time!"

"What did he say?" Haler asked Ted, but Ted merely grinned and shook his head, and Haler walked off with his nose out of joint.

They broke camp about noon and marched on into the narrowing passage of the Rio Grande, bucking snow that was growing deeper with every mile.

Ahead, the San Juans waited.

CHAPTER 13

The San Juans

PINES AND ASPENS GREW together on the level place where the expedition camped in four feet of soft snow. It was near the joining of two forks of the Rio Grande. Both water courses offered an attractive route deeper into the jumbled wedges of the Continental Divide. Except for the snow, it appeared that the expedition could travel on an easy grade for many miles.

At least, that was the way it looked to Ted that evening when he went out to Poche with a pocketful of corn filched from the dwindling sacks. With his back to the camp he sneaked the extra ration to the mule, while the other hungry animals came nosing in.

He saw sores on the backs of some of the mules, oozing sores that had partly scabbed over and then broken again under the chafing of the saddles. He looked at the grim wilderness of mountains yet to conquer, and for the first time since leaving Westport he wondered if the expedition could fail.

But when he looked toward camp and saw the fires, with strong, confident men roasting elk meat, laughing, accepting the hardships of camping in snow day after day without complaint, his moment of doubt passed on.

Why, aside from the mules, the expedition was tougher in spirit and body than it had been on the grueling marches across the Great Plains.

Haler met him at the edge of camp. "You've been sneaking corn to that favorite mule of yours again."

"Just a handful."

"Every kernel counts. You know the Colonel's orders."

"Go ahead, tell him!"

"I have to," Haler said. "It's my duty." He turned away with a smug look.

Haler *did* tell Colonel Frémont, but the Colonel apparently had more important problems on his mind than a handful of corn, for he merely instructed Godey to tell Ted not to exceed the pint ration of corn daily allowed each mule.

"I'll find cottonwood bark for him," Ted said. "No one can stop me from doing that."

But Ted had no chance to peel cottonwood bark for Poche, for the next day Old Bill led them away from the Rio Grande and into a small valley that came down from the right. Almost immediately the bellies of the mules were dragging snow.

Ted and Antoine were about midway in the long pack train. Antoine kept rising in his stirrups to look ahead over the swaying packs.

"What's the matter?" Ted asked.

The old man frowned. "It is a strange pass, I think." He shrugged. "Soon we will be in a bad place."

His prediction was borne out not long afterward when the valley pinched in suddenly with steep plunging slopes on both sides. The cavalcade had to cross and re-cross a small stream to squeeze out passage.

Sometimes there were ice bridges thick enough to hold the mules, but more often Old Bill's trail led down to shallow water through rounded snowbanks hanging above the stream. The packs of the leading mules gouged the fluffy banks of snow, cascading it into the creek where it was soon trampled into slush by the animals following.

The valley became a canyon. Tangles of beaver-cut aspens made the going very difficult. Every crossing of the stream was through the deep water of beaver ponds.

Old Bill, Colonel Frémont, and Godey had left the canyon. Ted could see them angling up a steep slope, but the pack train still had several crossings to go before it could leave the canyon.

The mules grew more reluctant about struggling across the stream, with sticky mud and silt trapping their feet and with ice cakes floating against their sides. Men had to dismount and lead them across, or walk beside them and urge them on.

"Move, move!" Proue shouted. "Keep heem moving or something freeze!"

After the first shock of wading in belly deep water, Ted was quite ready to agree with Proue that "something freeze." He didn't get back on his mule after that, for walking was the only way to keep from freezing inside his ice-coated clothing.

At one crossing the mules balked, with some of them already milling in the water. Men had to wade chest-deep among the floundering animals, shouting and urging them on, getting drenched shoulder-high by the plunging of the frantic animals as they lunged up the steep bank.

"What a place for a railroad!" McGehee said. He had been knocked completely under water by the struggling mules.

"Keep heem moving!" Proue shouted.

Move they did, fighting snow, icy crossings, and logs buried under the snow. Mittens were soaked. Hands were red and growing numb. Inside his frozen moccasins Ted kept working his toes in order to keep blood circulating in them.

From high up on the steep slope Colonel Frémont shouted the encouraging news that there was a ridge ahead which would offer better traveling.

One of the last creek crossings was the worst of all. Five or six mules went into it and then refused to go farther, even when men waded in with them and tried to urge them on. The animals had to be dragged out of the icy pool by means of ropes half-hitched around their tender muzzles.

"I have seen many passes," Antoine said, "but never one like this. Perhaps it is better farther on."

"At least it isn't as cold as it has been," Ted said hopefully.

From where he and Antoine stood, they could look back down the canyon and see part of the pack train strung out for a quarter-mile. Proue and others were wading in the bad crossing. A mule had slipped its pack, and the men were having a hard time.

"Move, move! Do not stand about!" Proue shouted.

Before the day was over, Ted was convinced that Old Bill certainly had not picked the best route through the San Juans, but maybe it was the quickest way, for they were going up rapidly.

The exertion of walking helped warm him, but he was grateful each time the mule ahead came to a stop. Some of the animals were trembling. At every stop a few of them brayed, as if they were trying to make the men understand how terrible their ordeal was. The sounds ran lonely over the icy canyons.

Someone was always shouting, "Move up, keep going!"

Though his legs and lungs told him how steep the climb was, Ted didn't realize how fast the expedition was gaining altitude until he looked back through a gap in the trees and saw how small the valley had become. Far away, the Sangre de Cristo was shining against a clear sky.

They toiled on, traversing the steep slope. Old Bill didn't seem to know about such things as zigzagging, for his trail held to a hard grade against the pitch of the mountain, swerving only to avoid trees or large outcrops of rocks.

Rocks that didn't show above the snow made the going dangerous for the shod mules. The iron shoes clanged and slipped.

Scrap fell at one such place where the churned snow hid a slanting outcrop. He sensed the treacherous footing and bunched himself to leap, but his hind feet slipped and he fell sidewise and skidded down the mountain.

Ted thought he would never stop, but the pack caught against two small trees that barely showed above the snow, and there Scrap lay, thrashing helplessly with his hind feet uphill.

Ted and Antoine worked their way down to him. The saddle had slipped. They had to dig through snow to find the cinch ring. Unstrapping the stiff cinch, Ted tore his fingernails. Blood dripped into the fluffy snow, piled against the belly of the mule.

"We must turn him around," Antoine said. "We must get his front feet uphill."

Ted glanced into the icy canyon. Its edge was about fifteen feet from where they stood.

"Take the front legs," Antoine said.

Their first effort to turn Scrap caused them and the mule to slide closer to the cliff.

It didn't seem to bother Antoine. "Again! Place your feet well so you do not slip."

Once more they heaved. Scrap brayed in terror as they

slid closer to the cliff, but they managed to get him partly turned. Antoine laughed and patted the mule's neck. "We will not throw you over the cliff, little one."

Ted wasn't so sure about that.

Again they strained to turn the mule. This time they got him around, front feet uphill. Ted got him around the neck and Antoine took him by the tail and they tugged to get him up. Scrap struggled to help himself. His efforts put them all closer to the edge.

Then the mule got its feet under him and came up with a surge that knocked Ted sprawling. To keep from going off the cliff, Antoine had to cling to Scrap's tail until the mule began to scrabble frantically back up toward the trail.

Antoine let go just in time, for when Scrap found good footing, he loosed a hearty kick at the Frenchman. "That one has the spirit to go to California," Antoine said.

Now the mule was back on the trail, but the heavy pack of cooking gear was still at the edge of the cliff. Tabeau and Wise came down to help. At first, they all tried to drag the pack uphill, but the footing was slick and the mountain steep, so they had to unload the cooking gear and carry it up piece by piece.

By then most of the pack train had gone on. Proue and King were coming up with the weak tail-enders. They waited while Antoine and Ted worked belt deep in the snow to pack Scrap.

Before the day was over, a dozen animals had fallen. Sometimes, when enough men were available, they could get a mule up, pack and all; more often, they had to do as Ted and Antoine had done with Scrap.

There seemed to be no end to the mountain.

"How far have we come today, Antoine?" Ted asked.

Antoine considered the question. "Four miles straight up, I think," he answered, grinning.

Soon afterward, one of the weaker mules collapsed. Shivering, it lay in the snowy trench.

"We must leave heem," Proue said.

The packers distributed the items from the exhausted mule's pack to the backs of the other animals. They rolled the mule to one side and the pack train went on.

Maybe he'll catch up later and be all right to-morrow, Ted told himself, but when he looked back, the mule was lying where they had left it.

Antoine touched Ted's arm. "There will be others."

By late afternoon the expedition had traversed the worst of the mountainside, but they were still on a slope so steep that when they camped, they had to bank up level places by using snow, packs, logs, and brush in order to sleep.

Pitching tents was out of the question. They spread the huge India rubber sheets—stiff and crackly and heavy—on the snowy sleeping places, threw down their blankets, and then covered them with another rubber sheet. By dusk, almost everyone would be in bed.

Since the first few days out from Westport, Ted had never been as tired as he was that late afternoon, when he helped unpack the mules. He doled out the corn rations for his mules, observing that Haler was watching him. The pint each mule received was hardly enough to sustain life.

At supper Ted saved half of his piece of lumpy bread. He planned to give it to Poche on the trail the next day, but when he heard the hungry braying of the mules, he waded back through the snow and gave the scrap to Poche, returning to the fire quickly.

While drying moccasins and leggings around the fires, men began to question Old Bill about the pass. From what they had heard, some of them thought it began much farther up the river than where they had turned away from the Rio Grande.

"You been there?" Old Bill challenged.

"No," Scott said, "but from what you said before . . ."

"I know where I'm going!" Old Bill growled.

Godey motioned for everyone to leave him alone.

Spraddle-legged at one of the fires, Captain Cathcart reached somewhere inside his woollen coat and pulled out a snow-white handerchief, neatly folded. He blew his nose and whisked the handkerchief away.

Then he noticed Doc Kern and several others staring at him. He swiped the backs of his hands across his mustache. "What's the matter? Have you never seen a nose the size of mine before?" His nose, indeed, was a most prominent part of his features.

Doc Kern laughed. "It was that white handkerchief, Captain. I'd forgotten there was such a thing."

Cathcart grinned. "Last one. After that's used, I'll find an Indian laundress. One of those Diggers Godey talked about."

A bright moon rose in the sky early. Sitting on a pack away from the fires, Dick Kern sketched a view of the country they had traveled that day.

Colonel Frémont was taking observations of the moon and stars, while Preuss assisted by holding a candle lantern close to the instrument. They were still at work after most of the men of the expedition were in bed.

It was a much warmer night than Ted had expected. As he lay in his blankets, close to Godey, he thought of the mule they had abandoned that day.

Maybe it could make its way back to the valley where it could paw for grass and nibble cottonwood bark. Then, if it survived the winter, perhaps in time it would wander into some settlement or be found by Indians who would eventually trade it off to white men.

Ted asked Godey about the mule's chances, and Godey replied sleepily, "It will die. From what Proue told me, I think it is dead by now."

The long winter night came down on the high country. Sometime during the dead quietness, when fires had burned low in their snowy pits, Old Bill roused up from a bad dream and cried out, "Hyar they come, Joe!"

"Shut up and go back to sleep," Breckenridge growled.

CHAPTER 14

Toward the Summit

WHERE THE DRIFTS WERE stacked so high that a mule could not break through, Old Bill pulled aside into the shelter of a clump of spruce trees and waited for the Colonel and some of the young men to break the way ahead.

"Straight on toward the top of the hill!" he yelled, pointing up toward the ever-rising mountain.

Godey and Taplin were among the forerunners who crashed through the huge drifts on foot, wallowing as the snow tumbled down on them like pouring smoke. They came back again, trampling a path for the mules.

They were young, Old Bill thought, full of energy and vinegar, so let them bust themselves. By old Ephraim, if he had used a lick of sense, he wouldn't be up here with a bunch of bright-eyed youngsters who thought the sun rose and set in Johnny Frémont.

He had a powerful effect on them, that Frémont; if he

said go, they went. Take a bunch of trappers in a fix like this, they'd scatter out of the hills mighty quick. But in the first place, a bunch of trappers wouldn't get in no fix like this, 'less they was caught by a quick snow and couldn't help it.

Old Bill watched Godey force his riding mule through the gap in the big snowdrift. The animal lunged and surged and made it through, sure enough, but then it stood trembling and heaving. That mule of Godey's was just about ready to go under.

On down the trail, the head of the pack train was coming.

"Is that the summit?" Colonel Frémont called, pointing.

Old Bill shook his head.

"How far is it then?"

"Three, four miles, I recollect." The Colonel was no greenhorn, Old Bill had to admit, but he was as bad as any pork-eater when it came to asking questions.

Taplin forced his mule through the snowdrift. It staggered and dislodged a great cascade of snow, so that when Taplin came up against Godey, he looked as if he'd been rolling down the mountain.

Old Bill rode through the gap. The top of the drift was about elbow high, with him on his mule. A heap of snow, and that was a mortal fact.

"She levels off some ahead," he said.

The whites of Frémont's eyes seemed enormous against his darkly bearded face. "Where do we start the descent?"

Old Bill waved. "When we get to the top." He could picture the land beyond, give or take a few ridges. It wasn't far until they'd go over a ridge and strike the headwaters of a little stream.

Colonel Frémont studied the guide. "You say then that we've broken the back of the ascent?"

"Yep." Old Bill spat past the neck of his mule. "Things depend now on the snow. We git through in about three days or we go broke."

They all knew what he meant. At this point the expedition was balanced between defeat and victory. Not many mules could last to return to the valley; it was drive ahead or give up.

Leading their mules, Godey and Taplin went on to break more trail.

Old Bill looked at the sky. "Hope it don't storm."

"Don't even think about it!" Frémont said.

Now it was December 14, 1848. Ted, Raphael Proue, and four others were far behind the main body, bringing along a bunch of weak mules.

Ted no longer had Scrap and Ney; they had been taken ahead to buck snow. But he still had Poche to help drag the faltering tail-enders up the worst of the pitches.

As far as he could see, the snowy trench led on and on toward the mountains, winding among the trees.

Leading Poche, Ted began to hurry up the trail, which was packed from the passage of hundreds of hoofs that had gone before.

"Too fast!" Proue shouted.

Ted stopped and looked around. He was fifty yards ahead of the weak mules.

"The others will not leave us behind," Tabeau said, sensing Ted's fear. The mule he was driving stopped. Tabeau asked for the rope that was tied to the crosstree of Poche's saddle.

Poche's strength was not what it had been, but he pulled strongly. The weak mule came along, but its trembling grew worse when they stopped to rest. Yellowish saliva was frozen on its muzzle. Its eyes were growing dim.

A hundred yards farther on, where the trail went up a sharp slant, the weak mule fell. Proue studied it only a moment before he said, "Off with the pack."

They took only shovels and axes from the pack. Before they left the hapless animal, Ted covered it with its blanket, although Proue waved his hand and said, "It is of no use."

Struggling on with the other exhausted mules, they reached easier traveling on a flat which bordered a mountain that thrust up on their left to a tremendous height. The rest of the expedition was not in sight, and the trail was a lonely scrawl that seemed to lead nowhere.

Then they began to pass abandoned equipment: packsaddles, blankets, canvas, cooking gear, and other items. Before long, they began to pass dead mules.

With late afternoon came wind and a piercing cold that filtered through dry garments and clung icily to wet leggings and pants. As he stumbled along, Ted kept working his toes vigorously. As long as he could feel a tingling in them, he figured they were not frozen.

With dusk only a short time away, Ted's fear grew, until he blurted, "Where are they? Where's the camp?"

Joaquin pointed toward trees a quarter-mile ahead. "Smoke," he said.

Ted could not see any smoke. "How do you know?"

Joaquin sniffed. "Smell smoke."

Ted peered anxiously through the gloom. He could neither smell nor see any evidence of fires in the dark timber ahead.

A weak mule fell. Ted removed his mittens to tie the tow rope around its neck. By the time they got the animal on its feet, Ted's fingers were so stiff from cold that he could not untie the rope.

"Move! Move!" Proue shouted.

Ted untied the knot with his teeth. In his hurry he gave up trying to fumble his numbed hands back into his mittens.

When they stumbled into the camp a half-hour later he went to the nearest fire and held his hands above the flames. In a few moments his fingers began to ache as if needles were being driven through them.

"Hold your hands above your head and work them," Godey said.

His advice was good. The pain began to leave Ted's fingers.

"Do not warm anything quickly when it is frozen," Godey said. "Better yet, do not let it freeze in the first place."

Though the expedition was camped in five feet of snow under a frowning mountain no one seemed dismayed. For supper there was boiled macaroni, elk meat, and plenty of coffee.

For the first time in several days, Colonel Frémont's lodge was set up. To Ted, that was an indication that everything was going about as expected.

That night it began to snow, as Ned Kern had predicted before he went to bed. Godey got up and went out to look at the weather. His going roused Ted, who lay for a while listening to the sound of the flakes on the lodge skins.

He thought of the night at Bent's Fort when he heard that Buffalo Hunter and the young Kiowas were out in the storm looking for Pawnees. Where was Buffalo Hunter now?

And Bent's Fort was a long, long way from here.

Godey came back into the lodge quietly.

"How does it look?" Colonel Frémont asked.

"Not so bad," Godey answered cheerfully, and returned to bed.

Ted heard the mules stomping around. They had been brought in close to the fires that night. Once more he heard the clacking of their ears as they shook their heads to keep their ears from freezing.

Early the next morning Colonel Frémont, Haler, and Godey went out with men to break trail toward what appeared to be the dividing ridge. Snow was falling, but not heavily, and the day was fairly comfortable.

Although he was once more at the tail end of the pack train, Ted had no fear of being left behind, for the whole expedition moved very slowly.

Through gusts of blowing snow, the ridge ahead was a beacon, a goal. Ted was no longer thinking of California, but only of the next mile or two.

Ned Kern had said that they were now close to twelve thousand feet high. Once over the top, they would go down; and even if the snow were still deep, surely they would find cottonwoods to provide feed for the mules and give them strength to fight on to grass.

During the first half-mile one of the mules at the rear of the train collapsed and died. One box of macaroni and a few handfuls of corn in a sack was the only salvage that Proue ordered removed from the dead animal.

As they fought on up toward the ridge, sometimes through drifts high above their heads, Ted realized what a terrible task the trail-breakers were facing. Some of them had carried shovels when they left camp, not for throwing snow out of the trail, but for beating it down.

Here, at the rear of the train, the trail was bad enough. If one of the mules lurched too far to one side, his legs would slip off the packed surface and he would fall helplessly against the side of the trench. It took back-breaking effort to get him going again.

Poche was showing the effects of the struggle. The grade was not severe, but Poche no longer went ahead briskly after each stop. Instead, he hesitated, as if gathering his strength before going on.

But there was the ridge up there above the last of the stunted trees; things would improve once they crossed that.

The trail was becoming littered with abandoned saddles and equipment. Dead mules lay beside it, the snow already drifting over their bodies.

Suddenly Ted asked Proue, "What would happen if we turned back?"

Proue shook his head. His beard was white with snow and his eyes were bloodshot. "The trail, she is blown full behind us. Colonel Frémont nevair turn back."

Near a twisted dead tree the trail bulged out to go around a dying mule. Ted glanced at the animal and then looked away quickly. He ploughed on another few steps and stopped. Dick! Godey's riding mule.

"Move, keep heem moving!" Proue said.

Seven animals died that day along the course of the two or three miles the expedition made. The ridge was still a quarter-mile above them when they camped on the side of a hill in the shelter of timber.

Corn rations were so low that each mule received but two handfuls. Before he went near the fires in the snow pits, Ted blanketed Poche and his other mules, feeling their pitiful boniness under the heavy coats of hair.

He gave the last few kernels of corn to Poche, and patted his neck. "Tomorrow we'll be going downhill, old fellow."

While the men ate macaroni and some of the last of the bacon, Colonel Frémont spoke confidently of getting across the pass in the morning.

The men at Ted's fire were quiet, but Ted saw no discouragement in their expressions; they believed Fré mont and still had faith in him as a leader. He had brought them this far, and there was no reason why he couldn't take them on to success.

Standing at one of the fires, eating macaroni from a tin plate with obvious distaste, Old Bill hunched around to stare at the darkening ridge above them.

CHAPTER 15

The Summit

TED WAS ONE OF the trail breakers who first gained the ridge. He stood on bare rock trying to look to the promised land beyond, but an ice-edged wind was driving snow in rolling billows that blotted out the view ahead.

The hairs in his nose felt like wires. The flesh of his cheeks was numb. He lowered his head to breathe, and even then the wind and the cold set his teeth on edge, and the air that went into his lungs felt like needles.

On an angling ascent they had beaten their way to this dividing ridge. Only a few of the strongest mules had made it with them. Already the animals were turning their rumps to the waves of snow and sliding back down the trail.

Ted looked around slowly. For a while the cold had been terrible, but now it didn't seem bad. His mouth opened and closed, as he tried to figure out what they were doing here.

Antoine's woollen coat was whipping around his knees. His eyes were squinted to slits. He struck Ted on the shoulder and pointed back down the trail. Ted nodded numbly, and then he sat down on a rock, lowering his head.

Other men were sitting down. They would rest for a time, Ted thought, and then they would go back; or perhaps they would go ahead to find a new camp. It didn't matter greatly, either way.

For one thing, it wasn't as cold now as it had been. Ted yawned.

Antoine beat him on the shoulder and shouted, "Get up!"

"In a minute." It seemed funny to see old Antoine stomping around in his long coat.

Antoine tried to lift him to his feet, and Ted tried to push the old Frenchman away. Then Godey came over. He helped Antoine drag Ted to his feet. They beat him on the back. They shoved him.

"You will freeze, idiot!" Godey shouted. "Walk!"

They held him up while he took a few stumbling steps. He wanted to sit down again, but they jerked him roughly and made him use his legs.

Scott, Martin, and Preuss were shouting at men, shaking them, forcing them to get up. Frémont and Cathcart were lifting Ducatel to his feet. Cathcart's mustache was a mass of ice. His big nose was white instead of its usual red. He slapped Ducatel and yelled at him.

Motion began to bring Ted back to his senses. He realized that he had been freezing without knowing it. "I'm all right now," he said. He knew that he had to get off the ridge.

Godey and Antoine left him and went back to help other numbed men. Beating his arms against his sides, Ted stumbled on toward the trail. His eyes were aching and his vision was disturbed.

Suddenly, out of the whipping sheets of white, Old Bill appeared on his mule. He was hunched in the saddle, with one arm shielding his face as he tried to peer ahead. Ted shouted at him, "Back! Everybody is going back!" The wind tore the words away, or else Old Bill didn't hear, for he paid no attention, but went on riding slowly along the ridge in the face of the blast.

Ted plunged down the trail. It was already filling with snow. He caught up with the mules. Preuss came up behind him. The German's face was red and wet with melted snow, and his mouth was drooping with anger. "That old fool, he wants to quit and die up there on the ridge!"

"Who?"

"Bill, the old fool!"

A moment later Ted almost bumped into a mule that was blocking the trench in a narrow place where the walls were six feet high. Behind him men began to shout angrily, "Go on, go on! We're freezing!"

Somewhere up ahead Scott yelled, "We're trying to get around a dead mule!"

Snow streamed down from the top of the trench,

while Ted and those behind him waited helplessly. Then
the mule in front of Ted went on again. It poised itself,
trembling, and then scrambled over a hump in the trail.
When Ted climbed over the obstruction, he realized that
it was the mule Scott had mentioned.

The still-smoldering fires in the camp were a welcome
sight. Men built them up quickly. Within a half-hour everyone was down from the near-fatal ridge, except Old Bill
and Godey.

They came in just when Frémont was detailing men
to go look for them. Godey was walking behind the guide's
mule. Old Bill was slumped across the saddle horn, very
nearly frozen to death. Men lifted him down and carried
him to one of the roaring fires, where soon he began to
thaw out, muttering to himself about the pass.

Preuss was off to one side, rubbing snow on his ears.
"Pass!" he snorted, and then he said something in German
which caused Creutzfeldt to smile quickly and look at
Colonel Frémont.

Almost everyone who had been on the ridge was
suffering from frostbite. Ted had white spots of frostbite
on his face, which he rubbed with snow. Thanks to the
deer hair in his moccasins, his feet had stayed warm all
day.

Willingly he helped set up the lodge, cutting and trim-
ming trees, and digging down through five feet of snow. A
sloping trench led upward from the doorway. When the
entrance was blocked with hides, a small fire inside was
enough to keep the lodge warm.

Colonel Frémont was moody that night. He was impatient with King when the latter made the daily report about supplies. He snapped at Preuss when the map maker suggested caching some of the equipment to lighten the mule packs.

As soon as Ted had eaten supper, he went to bed. In spite of his tiredness, he did not fall asleep at once. He listened to Frémont conferring with his lieutenants.

"It is now out of the question to turn back," Frémont said, "and I'm sure that none of you have been entertaining any such thoughts."

Haler shook his head vigorously.

"Only the small elevation we were on today separates us from the western drainage," Frémont continued. "Old Bill assures me that we will have no severe climbing from now on." He hesitated. "I know from my own previous experience that with every foot of altitude we lose the weather will improve. Tomorrow we'll go straight up the ridge, instead of traversing. The trail breakers will go first, as usual, push on to a suitable camp, and the mules will follow."

After those who slept outside the lodge had drifted away, Haler leaving last, Godey got into bed with Ted. Godey sighed long and wearily as he stretched out.

"You, my fine nephew, will stay with Proue and the other packers tomorrow. No more trail breaking for you. This is understood, yes?" Then, almost instantly, Godey fell asleep.

Only Preuss and Colonel Frémont were still up, Preuss sitting by the fire, writing in his diary.

Frémont said, "Someday you must translate that for

me, Preuss. You kept a diary on the first and second expeditions, too, didn't you?"

Preuss nodded. Ted got the impression that he was thinking that what he wrote in his diary was his own business.

"You remember when we crossed the Sierra Nevada in snow in 1843?" Frémont asked.

"We ate a little dog named Clammet. My mule was fat. Everyone ate him, too, except me. I remember."

Then Ted fell asleep.

In the morning they found five more mules dead in the snow. The hunger-driven animals had eaten anything they could find: saddle pads, their own blankets, ropes, and clothing hung on tree limbs to dry near the fires.

Immediately after breakfast the trail breakers went forth to attack the ridge. There was promise of a clear day, with only a light wind blowing. With shovels and with heavy limbs cut from trees, the advance party beat down the snow, packing it as they wallowed upward.

In the middle of the morning the mule detail once more tackled the ridge. The new trail was much steeper than the angling ascent of the day before. It took almost two hours to cover the quarter-mile to the crest.

Resting there on the bare rock, they looked ahead hopefully. This was the top they had almost killed themselves to reach, so they expected to be rewarded by a glimpse of fair going beyond.

Ted was disappointed. Sure enough, they would be going down for a while, but then the trail went up over another ridge; and beyond was nothing but winter, vast and deep as far as the eye could see.

"There's grass down there!" Andrews cried.

Ted squinted across the dazzling white expanse. Sure enough, there was grass showing beyond the point of the next rise. It was an encouraging sight.

Through drifts sometimes ten feet high they floundered down the trail. Saddles slipped continually, because there were no pads under them. Getting them in place again caused long delays.

Even before the animals ate their pads, their backs had been galled; now they were masses of frozen scabs and running sores from the rubbing of the wooden saddles. That morning Ted had pulled parts of blankets from under dead mules to make pads for Poche and Scrap.

After three hours they reached the next ridge. The trail beaters were working on ahead toward a small valley. The wind was rising and the sky was a dirty gray. Snow streamed from the clubs and shovels of the work detail hammering at the drifts.

"There's more grass!" Andrews shouted.

Everyone took heart at the sight. But when the pack train toiled on to the place where they thought grass was growing, they discovered only the tops of mountain mahogany, a willow-like shrub that was sticking above five feet of snow. That was the grass.

And a storm was building in the west.

Godey met the pack train on a rocky point. "Unpack here. We'll drag what we need down to camp."

After unpacking, they drove the mules a short distance beyond the campsite to a knoll where wind had blown the snow away, exposing a small area of grass.

Snow fell during the night. But at daylight the weather gave some promise of clearing. Frémont sent the trail breakers down the valley. When the packers went up the knoll to feed the mules, Ted counted fifteen dead animals. The survivors were eating each other's tails and manes.

It was December 17, 1848. Before noon, a new storm drove the trail breakers back to camp. For seven nights the expedition was to stay in the same camp. For five days it stormed, relenting only for short periods. The trail behind filled with snow.

Those who shared Frémont's lodge, as the snow piled higher, were snug and warm. In the pits where the others lived in small groups, the days and nights were misery.

Men's faces were black with soot. Their eyes were inflamed from smoke. They slept in soggy blankets. At times, they groped their way from the holes to rub their eyes with snow and breathe air not filled with smoke—and to look hopefully for a break in the weather.

Now they were eating mule meat.

On the third day, in the place they were to name Camp Desolation, only fifty-nine mules were still alive. Though they were starving, it was really cold that killed them. Seeking both food and warmth, some of the animals tried to force their way down from the windy knoll to the camp.

Most of them died on the way.

While watching Scott and Martin butchering one of

the frozen mules, Preuss said in surprise, "There's still fat on him!" He nodded. "Ah so, it takes a very long time for any animal, including us, to die of starvation. Of course, the cold contributes greatly to . . ."

"I don't care what he died of!" Scott said. He put his aching hands under his arms to warm them. "You scientific fellows figure out what killed him. All I know is you can freeze your hands butchering him."

Every night more mules died. A few of the stronger survivors fought through the snow to the camp. They tried to eat blankets and clothing. They nosed into the cooking utensils. The men had to drive them back to the bare hill.

Ted was eating warmed-over macaroni for breakfast one morning when he heard a shot. He walked outside and saw Haler standing with a smoking rifle near a dead mule. Though it was not the first animal that had been killed for food, Ted stared in horror. He thought the dead mule was Poche.

Almost blind with rage, he started to rush toward Haler. Antoine caught him by the coattail. "Wait! That is not one of your pets."

When he took a better look, Ted realized that it was not Poche.

"It's easier to butcher them while they're warm," Haler said, drawing his knife. Ferguson came out of a snow pit carrying an axe.

Sick with revulsion, Ted turned away, swearing that he would never eat a piece of mule meat, no matter how hungry he was.

CHAPTER 16

Defeat

ON THE NIGHT OF December 21st, Colonel Frémont made his decision to turn back. He called his leaders to the lodge and, after Jackson served them with coffee, Frémont made his announcement.

"Until we have fresh animals it will be impossible to continue, so I have decided to descend to the Rio Grande with all our baggage, there to regroup until we are able to resume the exploration."

Taplin stopped in the act of raising his cup to his bearded face. He stared. "You mean to go on, Colonel?"

"Of course!"

"I mean over *these* mountains?"

"Yes!" Frémont said. "By a different route, to be sure. We've already conquered what is possibly the worst pass

138

in all the San Juans. Only extremely bad weather has pre-
vented us from now being forty to fifty miles closer to
California. Even if we have to turn north to the Cochetopa, we've already succeeded, as far as I'm concerned."

Wise said slowly, "I take it that we'll go back down
to the Rio Grande some other way than the route we came
up?"

Frémont nodded. "Yes. Tomorrow Alex and Breckenridge will lead a party to break trail to the head of one of
the streams northeast of here. The rest will follow with
the baggage as soon as possible."

"You mean we're going to try to save all the baggage?"
Taplin asked.

"Of course. The expedition will go on just as quickly
as I can secure mules from Taos or one of the nearby settlements."

"How far is it to Taos?" Haler asked.

"Possibly a hundred and twenty miles," Frémont said.

Ted thought of the long, bleak valley down which
Antoine had pointed when the expedition was crossing the
Sangre de Cristo. At least there hadn't been much snow
there, compared with this place.

"A hundred and forty," Preuss said. He puffed at his
pipe, staring at a map.

"We have more than sufficient provisions to last us
down to the river and for a safe period thereafter," Frémont said. "With renewed supplies and fresh animals, I
haven't the least doubt that we can continue almost as
planned."

That Colonel Frémont was a great leader, Ted never doubted, not even when he went outside after the meeting and saw the smoke drifting above holes where men huddled half-blind.

Old Bill came out of a pit, gnawing a piece of bloody mule meat. Gaunt faced, with straggly red whiskers, he looked like a scarecrow suddenly thrust up from the snow. "What's going on in there, bub?"

"We're going back to the river, Mr. Williams."

Old Bill grinned like a wolf. "Thought so, I did!"

Activity revived the spirit of the expedition. Men were glad to crawl from their pits and resume the struggle. The trail breakers went back across the ridge by a new route, and then angled off northeast toward timber at the head of a small creek.

Dragging some baggage with them, the pioneer party that first day reached a new camp about two miles away, while those left at Camp Desolation made preparations to move.

Twelve mules were still alive, Poche among them.

For three days everyone labored to get the baggage back over the ridge and on to the new camp, which was to be called Camp Hope. They relayed the packs, stronger men carrying eighty pounds on their backs.

Food supplies were still sufficient to last until a relief party could make a round trip to one of the New Mexican settlements.

On Christmas Day men brought out carefully hoarded delicacies: flour, rice, the last of the elk meat; and there was plenty of mule meat, which by then Ted was eating with good appetite.

That night, Colonel Frémont picked his men for the long trip to bring relief.

Old Bill was to guide them. He sat before the fire in Frémont's lodge and took the opportunity to dry his moccasins while listening to the talk.

"I've calculated each campsite on the way down the river," Frémont said. "Allowing for any natural delays, I've figured sixteen days to the Red River settlements and back to the Rio Grande at a point near where we entered the mountains. How does that strike you, Bill?"

"Close enough, Colonel. We ought to reach the river in one day from here."

"I've allowed three," Frémont said.

Old Bill shrugged.

"King will be in command of the party. Creutzfeldt and Breckenridge will be the other two men. I want you to stay with the river, to travel as swiftly as possible, and of course to return without delay."

"Expect to," Old Bill grunted.

"One other point. If there should be a delay in arranging for mules and provisions, King, I want you to send a messenger back at once, advising me of the situation. Now is that quite clear?"

"Good enough, Colonel," King said.

"There is a possibility that Indians may give you some trouble, although it is unlikely that they'll be roaming the valley in any great force." Frémont hesitated. "Bill, I'm somewhat concerned because of your difficulties last fall with the Utes. I'm wondering how your presence with the party will affect . . ."

"I can handle any Utes that show up!" Old Bill said. He rose. "If you don't think I can get down there and back, just say so!"

Frémont held his temper. "I do want you to go. I was merely considering . . ."

"Ain't no use to consider too much," Old Bill growled. "I'll take your party to Abiquiu or Taos—or wherever we have to go—and see they get back too. If that ain't good enough . . ."

"It's good enough," Frémont said.

Old Bill walked out of the lodge.

Godey said thoughtfully, "I think I should go along."

"No," Frémont said. "I need you here."

Taplin spoke up strongly. "Colonel Frémont, I think it's a mistake for us to try to get all the packs down to the river. It took over a hundred mules to bring that stuff up here, and now the men are in no condition to . . ."

"All the baggage will be taken to the river. Without it, the expedition is lost. You must understand, Taplin, that we are not defeated. We are only reorganizing."

"We may be dead-out beat before we ever get all the baggage to the Rio Grande," Taplin insisted.

Ted was sitting on a heavy wooden case that held books Frémont had brought along. He thought perhaps Taplin had a point.

Frémont tried persuasively to change Taplin's view

about the baggage. Taplin fell silent, but it was obvious that his mind was unchanged. From that day on there was a coolness between the two.

Under clear skies the next morning men crawled out of their snow holes to give a ragged cheer to the four-man party, as it set out to bring relief.

They were traveling light: their weapons, two blankets each, and a small bundle of food. Godey was leading the way, but he was going only a short distance to pick a trail for the main body of the expedition to follow later.

The party toiled down toward the beginnings of a stream where mountain mahogany showed above the snow. Godey fell back, giving way to Breckenridge, a powerful man of medium build. King, strong and wiry, was behind Godey then, and next Creutzfeldt.

Old Bill slouched along at the rear, the ears of his blanket cap flapping in the wind. He looked from side to side, as if hopeful of seeing game.

Snow swirled around them playfully. Slowly, the party worked their way down the creek, along a wooded hill, and disappeared from view.

Ted thought of the long miles facing them, twelve to the river, perhaps, then one hundred and thirty or forty to some town, and then the long return.

For once, he was relieved to hear Haler's voice.

"No use to stand gawking after them, boy. We've got work to do."

That day Poche was too weak to drag anything. To the very last, a mule named Polly continued to struggle up and down the trail dragging baggage, and then she too gave out and was left in camp near one of the fires. The ears of both animals had been frozen and now they drooped.

As long as he lived, Ted would remember the sounds of freezing, starving mules shaking their heads when their ears were lumps of ice.

From the ridge, where men painfully gathered loads of baggage, they could see a few mules still standing forlornly on the windy knoll near Camp Desolation.

"I guess we'll soon be eating your favorite mule," Haler said.

"You shut up!"

Haler looked innocent and hurt, but behind his innocence lay a sly, cruel expression.

Taplin was just turning to leave with a pack. He put it down in the snow and said, "We're all filthy on the outside, Haler, but you've got it on the inside as well."

"I just said . . ."

"Another time and I'd break your teeth." Taplin hoisted his pack again, staggering. "Come on, Ted."

Five mules were still with the expedition when the trail breakers led the way downward the next morning. The new camp was in a little valley, slightly more than a mile from Camp Hope.

The hardest blow struck Ted McNabb two days after Christmas. Four mules were left: Poche, John, a chunky gray that Doc Kern had gotten from the Indians at Big Timbers, and a tall blue mule named Mike.

Poche barely made it to camp that day. Ted knew that the mule would never last to the river. He looked at Poche quietly, remembering the powerful, ornery brute from the start of the expedition. Without tail or mane, with his legs cracked and bleeding, with his frozen ears hanging loosely, Poche was a pitiable object.

Ted got his rifle. He raised it and could not pull the trigger.

Behind him Godey said quietly, "Yes, that is the thing to do."

A cloud of foul powdersmoke rose from the muzzle of the rifle when Ted fired. He took one glance at Poche lying in the snow, with the wind stirring the long hair on his flanks.

Ted turned away. He bumped into Colonel Frémont, who gave him a look of understanding and gripped him by the shoulder for an instant.

Ted was thankful that Jackson was the only one in the lodge when he stumbled inside, for by then he was crying. He was fourteen, but he had stood up under the hardships of the expedition as well as anyone, and he had been doing a man's work. Now he was crying, and he felt that he was showing weakness.

Jackson glanced at him, and then went back to sewing a patch on a worn moccasin.

After a time, Ted gained control of himself. "I couldn't help it."

"Sure enough." Jackson rose and poured Ted a cup of coffee. "The man who don't cry because he thinks he's too strong to be a human being ain't much good, and that's a fact."

CHAPTER 17

Starvation

THE EXPEDITION BROKE INTO groups. In the lead were Frémont, Godey, Preuss, Jackson, and Ted. Sometimes miles
behind were the three Kern brothers, Gregorio, Joaquin,
and Captain Cathcart. In between came the main body.

Men passed and re-passed each other, going back and
forth to relay baggage down the trail. Sometimes, when
late afternoon caught them or great weariness from dragging baggage up and down ridges, individuals from one
camp would stop for the night in another camp.

Old Bill had thought he would reach the river in one
day with the relief party, but the marks of his camps, found
by Godey, showed that the advance group had not been
traveling as fast as Old Bill had planned.

No admirer of Old Bill, Preuss stomped around with
a scowl when he saw the first campsite of the relief party.

146

"At this rate they took four days to get to the river. That old fool may lose his way again."

"He will not!" Frémont said. "All they have to do is follow the Rio Grande. Even without Old Bill, King can be depended on to do that."

Fighting the baggage every inch of the way, the shattered expedition kept working down toward the river. The descent was not easy, for there was no natural trail downward. Sometimes they got too far into canyons and had to crawl out again. At other times they were able to sit on the baggage and ride it down steep hills, shouting happily as gravity did the work.

For a week after Christmas, clear, warm weather prevailed, and this caused the snow to settle considerably. In some places it was only two feet deep. There was always plenty of timber for fires.

That was on the good side. Then, too, Old Bill and King were undoubtedly far on their way down the San Luis Valley, and might even return with mules and provisions sooner than the time limit allowed by Frémont.

But on the bad side was the ominous fact that food supplies were going fast. There was macaroni, saltside, sugar, coffee, and some mule meat, along with odds and ends of food that men had stored privately; but there would be a few hungry days, even if Old Bill and King returned on time.

Alexis Godey began to sense something worse than lack of food. He spent much of his time going back up the trail to encourage stragglers, and he observed that more baggage was being abandoned every day, packsaddles first, then cooking gear and tents—even rifles that grew too heavy to carry.

Godey saw the growth of something else that was more deadly than exhaustion, a breaking of spirit. They had been heroes going up the mountain and they had started the descent with high confidence, but now this struggle with the baggage and a growing shortage of food . . .

A sudden storm came from the west and drove the scattered men to shelter. In a camp among cottonwoods Godey found Martin, Scott, and Taplin.

"We're taking too long coming down," Scott said. "Food is short. Men are getting scared, Alex. For the first time they're afraid of what might happen to us all."

"Supplies will come," Godey said. More than ever he wished Frémont had let him go with the relief party.

"Suppose Old Bill and the rest ran into Utes?" Martin asked.

Godey smiled. "They have seen Indians before." He spoke confidently, though he knew that Colonel Frémont was worried over the very thing that Martin had wondered about.

"I think we're in a fix," Scott said moodily.

A cold wind blew through the bare trees and a shower of frost crystals came down on the makeshift shelters, where men crouched before fires.

"We should have brought more mule meat with us— and forgotten all about the equipment," Taplin said.

"We had food to last us," Godey said. "We still have

enough. King will be here, do not fear." He counted noses around the cheerless camp. "Where's Proue?"

"Far back with the Kerns," Scott said. "The three Indians are there, too." He shook his head. "Manuel's feet are very bad."

On January 2, 1849, Frémont's lead party reached the river and set up the lodge which Ted and Jackson had dragged from the mountains. At times they had talked of pushing it into a canyon and forgetting it, but now they were glad that they had not, for they would be able to live in comfort until King's party returned.

Snow came again. Biting cold struck. Then more snow.

The expedition was scattered along the small stream they had followed from the mountains, Frémont's party near the Rio Grande and the Kerns far behind in the lower hills.

On January 10th, Godey came into Frémont's lodge after a visit to the main camp seven miles up the little creek. Ted knew from his expression that he had bad news.

"Proue is dead."

Frémont was sitting near the fire writing. "What!"

"Yesterday afternoon he tried to come on down to the river. He gave out on the flats. Haler found him there and tried to get him up, but he couldn't, so Haler covered him with blankets and came on. When he went back, Proue was dead."

Ted had never seen Colonel Frémont so affected. He seemed to be on the verge of tears. "Proue was with me on all my expeditions. He was one of the best men I ever had. I just can't believe that he would lie down in the snow and die."

"That's Haler's story. I think there may be other reasons for his death," Godey said. "I know he was worn out."

"But to lie down like that and give up . . ." Frémont shook his head. "Did he have matches?"

"Yes."

"Then he must have quit."

"I don't think so," Godey said. "Even before we reached Bent's Fort he told me he hadn't been feeling well."

Haler could have done more for Proue than leave blankets and go on, Ted thought. He could have built a fire, forced Proue to rise and walk, as Antoine and Godey had done for him when he was freezing.

Frémont was in a dark mood the rest of the afternoon. Proue's death weighed heavily on him. That night he said to Godey, "I'm afraid something has delayed King."

There was no need to discuss the many reasons why the relief party might be late, or not return at all; everyone in the lodge had gone through that before. And they knew that in the camps upstream men were eating candles, rawhide, and strips of leather from their clothing.

"I am very sure he is delayed," Godey said.

"If he doesn't come tomorrow, we'll strike out." Frémont looked around the lodge. "The five of us will go. The expedition must have relief as soon as possible."

Ted looked hopefully down the river the next morning for the sight of mules coming through the snow. He
remembered how easily Poche had covered that same
ground, bearing a three-hundred-pound pack.

No moving forms showed. Cottonwoods. The frozen
river. And far away, the gleaming peaks of the Sangre de
Cristo.

This day had been set for the arrival of the relief party.
There was no magic in that, but still men hoped—and
tried to believe the party would be on time. So strong was
the thought, that Haler and a few others arrived early at
the lodge to welcome King's pack train; and the Kerns believed enough to try and struggle down to the river from
their distant camp to greet the relief party.

Men stood outside the lodge, shading their eyes
against snow glare, their faces turned to the south. They
watched and waited until the hope in their expressions
turned to bitterness and fear.

In the middle of the morning Colonel Frémont wrote
an order and gave it to Haler to take back to the other
camps.

"We can wait no longer," the Colonel told Haler. "I
am proceeding down the river immediately to get help.
You will be in charge of the expedition, Haler. Direct the
men to bring all the baggage down to the lodge here and
store it. If, by that time, you have not heard from me, follow my trail down the Rio Grande with the remaining
men."

Ted could see Haler's sense of importance grow the
moment he knew he was being left in charge. Ted thought,

I'm glad I'm not going to stay behind, with *him* running things.

"Then we're not going to try the San Juans again, Colonel?" Haler asked.

"There's no reason to," Frémont answered. "I've determined as much as I need to know about them. I want you to make it clear to everyone that this is still an expedition. My plans have changed, but I'm not quitting."

"Yes sir!" Haler said crisply.

Preuss looked at him with an expression of disgust.

January 11, 1849 was the day Colonel Frémont set out with the second relief party, which included Godey, Preuss, Jackson and Ted. They left half of their scanty food supply to be divided among the men remaining at the camps. They took their rifles, two blankets each, and food to last two days.

They followed the frozen river, walking for the most part on the ice, where snow was less deep than along the banks.

By any reckoning it was well over a hundred miles to the nearest settlement, but at first they were still hopeful of meeting King's party returning with food.

Trudging along on the ice, Frémont said that he now planned to go to California by a southern route, just as soon as he could get the expedition reorganized.

"Reorganized?" Preuss grumbled. "First it must be rescued."

That afternoon Godey discovered day-old horse tracks on the bank of the river. "It must be King's messenger!" Frémont cried.

Further study of the tracks showed that the horse had turned downriver almost at the very point where Godey first saw the marks. "He quit before he found us!" Frémont said. Preuss was of the same opinion.

Godey continued to study the tracks carefully. "I don't think it was the messenger from King. It could have been, but why would he turn back after coming this far? I think an Indian hunter made those tracks."

"It was the messenger," Preuss said gloomily.

Godey's contention that the tracks had been made by an Indian pony seemed to be borne out later, when he found an Indian camp made a week or ten days previously.

And then, on an island overgrown with willow trees, Frémont found another campsite which he took to be one of the places where King's party had stopped.

The discovery of the two sites so close together worried Frémont's men. They knew that the Utes hated Old Bill, and that might have caused the whole advance group to be killed by the Indians.

"In the morning we'll follow that Indian trail until we find their camp," Frémont said.

They did not overtake the Indians the next day. Frémont was limping badly on a leg frostbitten two weeks before, and the rest of the party was tiring. On the following day they ate the last of their food. Now they had only coffee left.

Against the glaring white of the great valley they toiled on. Ted's rifle was growing heavier with each step. He kept shifting it from one shoulder to the other. For a while he had tried to watch the willow thickets for game, but gradually he had lost interest. Concentrating on the work of moving one foot ahead of the other, he considered throwing away his rifle.

Jackson was ahead of him. His worn-out moccasins were wrapped in blanket strips. He stumbled as he walked. Ted decided to give his last spare pair of moccasins to Jackson when they stopped to rest.

Colonel Frémont was limping so badly now that Ted wondered if he could keep going much longer. If they had to stop because of a storm, cold and lack of food would finish them quickly.

Ted thought of Proue. Sick and hungry, he had laid down, and in no time he was dead.

"Carefully now. Do not excite him," Godey said in French. "It is of the greatest importance that he does not take alarm."

The party was stopped, Ted realized suddenly. He raised his head to see what Godey was talking about. A deer perhaps! That would be wonderful.

There was no deer.

An Indian youth on a shaggy pony was watching them from the edge of an opening among the willows.

Both Frémont and Godey made signs of peace. The youth responded hesitantly, poised between staying and flight. Slowly, Frémont and Godey went toward him. They spoke in Ute and then in Spanish.

The Indian had an arrow laid across his bow. Then, deliberately, he dropped it over his shoulder into the quiver. He rode toward the two white men.

The Ute's name was Cuerno. He said he knew of the white men and many mules that had gone into the mountains, and he was surprised to see five of them still alive. His father's camp was not far away. Yes, he would guide them to it.

They reached the Indian camp the next day and were made welcome. The Ute leader knew Frémont from a previous trip when they had met on the Grand River. Though the food supplies of the Indians were meager, they shared what they had.

The Indians knew nothing of King's party. "Gone under," the leader said. "Much snow, cold, little game."

Frémont traded most of his personal equipment for four ponies. He hired Cuerno as a guide, and the party resumed their trip that afternoon.

They were spurred on by the probability that King's group was dead, and that the rescue mission now rested entirely on their shoulders.

Their luck improved. Godey killed a deer, and for the first time Ted was able to eat raw liver without gagging.

Near the mouth of the Conejos River, on January 17th, they saw smoke ahead in the trees. Another Indian camp, Ted thought.

They rode into the grove.

A man, crouched behind a log, rose suddenly, waving his rifle and shouting in a shrill voice. He was a ragged, filthy creature, with matted beard and knobby, blistered cheekbones. He hopped around on feet wrapped in blanket strips.

"It's the Colonel, boys!" he shouted.

Ted was sure he had never seen the man before, but Frémont said in a shocked voice, "Bill!"

Ted stared at the man in horror. At first he could not believe the wild figure was Old Bill Williams.

Another man came hobbling forward, dropping his rifle.

"Breckenridge!" Godey said.

Breckenridge could hardly walk. His bare legs were a mass of running sores, and his bearded face was pinched and gaunt. He babbled incoherently as he staggered forward to fall on Frémont's shoulder. "I knew you'd come, Colonel. I kept telling them all the time!"

"Where's King?" Frémont asked.

Breckenridge lurched away and went back to the fire, where a third man was crouched, pawing at his eyes and watching the scene suspiciously. Breckenridge helped the man to his feet and led him forward. "It's all right, Fred! It's the Colonel!"

"Who is it?" Frémont asked.

"Creutzfeldt!" Breckenridge said.

Ted hadn't recognized him either. Creutzfeldt kept rubbing at his eyes. Flesh was peeling from frostbitten places on his face and hands.

"Where's King?" Godey said.

Old Bill pointed toward the backtrail. "He played out and died. Creutzfeldt went back after him, but he was dead."

They helped the survivors back to the fire. Cracked deer bones were lying by the flames. Shreds of blankets hung on the trees. Ted kicked aside some of the bones to make a place to sit down.

Creutzfeldt scrabbled over like an animal and snatched up the bones and held them against his chest, snarling like a dog.

CHAPTER 18

Rescue

AFTER FEEDING THE STARVING men and wrapping their
swollen feet in blankets, Colonel Frémont put them on
the Indian ponies and the whole group, still guided by
Cuerno, set out for the nearest pueblo. It was too far to
Abiquiu now; Frémont decided to gamble on finding help
at one of the tiny settlements north of Taos.

Old Bill blamed the failure of the relief party on King,
who he said was unable to travel more than a few miles
each day after they got out of the San Juans.

"We had to stop and hunt, and there warn't nothing
to find," Old Bill said. "Starving times, do ye hear? We ate
our belts. We gnawed at the grease on our knife cases. We
ate our moccasins, because we couldn't stand to have them
on our froze feet no longer.

"Then we had to keep tearing up our blankets to wrop

around our feet. Come night, we set in a hole in the snow
with our feet together and what little covering we had left
drawed over us."

Old Bill and Breckenridge told a shocking story of
their hardships. Half blind, growing weaker, suffering the
agony of frostbitten feet and legs, they had crawled at
times on their way down the river.

A few days before Frémont found them, Breckenridge
had killed a deer, which lasted only a short time before
they were starving again.

"I still don't understand why you traveled so slowly
the first week," Frémont said. "We had to face the same
conditions, too, but we . . ."

"You'd been sleeping in a warm lodge," Old Bill said
testily. "You found horses, too. After you came out of the
mountains, you rested for a spell, while we came straight
on down the river. Even so, if King hadn't started to play
out . . ."

"There were times when it was you, Bill, who couldn't
get out of camp," Breckenridge said accusingly.

"Warn't so!" Old Bill growled.

There was a strong difference of opinion as to what
had caused the failure of the first relief party; the reasons
would never be clear to Ted. It seemed to him that both
Old Bill and Breckenridge had things on their minds they
didn't care to discuss.

Creutzfeldt could contribute nothing. His mind was
shaken by the ordeal.

Camped one night in a bend of the Rio Grande, Old
Bill bemoaned the lack of tobacco. His feet and legs were

sickening to look at, but he declared, "Meat grows back fast in this country, but tobacco don't grow here no way."

"Them Indians might have had tobacco," Breckenridge said, "but you wouldn't let us . . ."

"We'd all be under if we'd gone to them Utes!" Old Bill said heatedly.

"Oh, you *did* see signs of Indians?" Frémont asked.

"I seen their smoke in a bend of the river, but Utes don't shine to me no more. We cut across the bend to get past." Old Bill nodded. "That's when King played out."

Creutzfeldt edged up. "King! Yes, he was dead when I went back to him. He lay in the snow just the way he fell down. He was dead." He seemed to be rational, but his mind soon slipped back, and he retreated to the opposite side of the fire, staring.

"I guess the Indians would have rubbed us out," Breckenridge said. "Well, we're all right now."

The snow thinned out as they followed the banks of the river southward. There was a pueblo three camps away, on the river, Cuerno said. The party took no chances by heading toward it in a direct line; they played safe and took the longer route beside the stream.

Frémont's limp grew worse each day. Once more food supplies ran out. But that same afternoon Cuerno stopped on the crest of a small rise, pointing, and when the others came up to him, they saw smoke from adobe houses not far away.

Godey's thoughts were already running far beyond immediate comforts. He was thinking of the men left on the

Rio Grande when he said, "It looks too small, Colonel, to supply the mules we're going to need."

With true Mexican courtesy the little village received the gaunt, crippled men of the fourth expedition.

That afternoon Ted ate tortillas and goat stew until he could eat no more, and then all at once he was so sleepy he could hardly hold his head up. An old Mexican woman made a bed for him in the corner near the fireplace, and as he lay down he heard Godey saying something to Preuss about having to go to Taos.

It was night when Ted woke up. Preuss was sitting at a table eating, and the sight made Ted even hungrier than he had been before. "Where's Alex?"

"He went to Taos for mules," Preuss said. He took a big bite of goat meat. "I wish I had some German food. Terrible, so many peppers in everything they cook here." He patted his stomach. "Good though!"

Ted joined Preuss at the table and helped himself to cold tortillas. He wondered if he would ever get enough to eat. "Who's going back with my uncle?"

"He will find men. Kit Carson perhaps. The people here say that he is in Taos."

"I'll go."

Preuss studied the boy slowly. "Yes, you would go. I would go too, but it is not necessary. Godey will arrange things. He is made of iron, your uncle."

Though he had just wakened, Ted felt exhaustion overtaking him again. The days and nights in the San Juans, the snow and cold seemed far away. The bearded, hollow-eyed faces of the men still out in the snow floated hazily through his mind.

"We lost, didn't we?" he asked.

"All the equipment, the mules—thousands of dollars thrown away. And men." Preuss shrugged. "Against those mountains we lost everything."

Ted was so drowsy he could not hold his head up.

Preuss said, "But perhaps he is right when he says we are not defeated at all."

Ted fell asleep with his head on the table and a half-eaten tortilla in one hand.

The Survivors

LATER ON TED LEARNED that Alexis Godey was indeed a man of iron. He had rested in the little village overnight, and then, not finding enough mules and horses there, had ridden on the next morning with Colonel Frémont to Taos, twenty-five miles away. So changed was Frémont by his hardships that at first Kit Carson hadn't recognized him.

Getting mules and horses and some Mexican packers to assist him, Godey loaded up provisions and was back in the little village the next evening, where he laughed away Ted's offer to accompany him on the rescue mission.

Godey started up the Rio Grande the next morning. He overtook two Mexican traders on their way to Ute camps with bread and meal, and enlisted their services.

He was making twenty miles a day, as the crow flies, but actually a great many more miles, because he was

holding close to the river, knowing that the surviving members of the expedition would not go far from the stream.

On the third day out he met Joaquin and Gregorio,
lank-ribbed and near exhaustion, but still on their feet.
Slender men of wiry strength, the California Indians had
not given way to panic on the starvation trek down the
river. They probably would have made it to safety without
help.

Godey gave them food and waited impatiently for
them to cook it.

"Haler, one camp," Joaquin said, pointing upriver.
He explained that he and Gregorio had stayed with the
Kerns at first, and then with the men in Haler's group,
hunting for them and trying to urge them along.

"Where are the Kerns now?" Godey asked.

"Far away," Joaquin said. He added that the expedition had broken into several groups after starting from the
camps at the base of the San Juans.

That was bad news, Godey thought. It showed that
Haler's authority had not held up, or else he hadn't exer-
cised command properly. The best chance of survival had
been for everyone to stay together.

Godey studied the Indians as they roasted pork on
sticks over a fire. "Why did you leave Haler?"

Joaquin and Gregorio looked at each other. "Eat us,
maybe," Joaquin said darkly.

"Where's Manuel?" Godey asked quickly.

"Dead, him," Gregorio answered.

He explained that Manuel had been able to go only a
short distance after they came out of the San Juans. The

CHAPTER 19

bottoms of his feet were falling off from frostbite, and he knew that he would never be able to make the long trip through the snow downriver.

He had begged Haler to shoot him, but Haler would not do that, so on the day all the others started down the Rio Grande, Manuel turned back to his last camp. Joaquin and Gregorio went with him, giving him most of their food and gathering firewood for him—and then they had left him.

"Wise, him dead too," Joaquin said. "Fall down on the ice and die." He and Gregorio, catching up with the expedition after doing what they could for Manuel, had found Wise lying on the frozen river. They had buried him under snow and willows on the bank of the stream.

It was now January 26th. From what the two Indians told him, Godey calculated that the survivors had left their camps at the foot of the mountains ten days before. Some of them had been dying even then. Those still alive would be strung for a considerable distance along the river.

"How were the Kerns and Cathcart when you left them?"

Joaquin shook his head. "No food. Weak."

"Eat the rest of that while you're riding," Godey said. "Let's go."

The next day he found Haler, Ducatel, Bacon, and Martin starving in a wretched camp. They staggered to their feet with glad shouts, and then they cried like children.

With difficulty, Godey restrained them from gorging themselves sick on the food he distributed. Since Haler was the only one fit to travel, Godey decided to leave food and horses and let the party stay where it was until he could return from picking up the other survivors.

He received Haler's version of what had happened on the disastrous trip downriver.

"We had to split up," Haler said. "Some men couldn't keep up, so the rest of us went ahead for help."

"You knew help would be coming. You should have stayed together."

"They defied my authority," Haler complained. "Some of them insisted on going it alone. Antoine and old Tabeau tried to go ahead of everyone, but they wore themselves out and died."

Antoine and Tabeau dead. It was a blow to Godey. First Proue, and now the other two tough old veterans. "You're sure they're not behind with some of the others?"

"They were in bad shape." Haler shook his head. "One day Tabeau couldn't make it into camp. Antoine went back after him. We never saw them again."

"You sent no one back to help?"

"I couldn't!" Haler whined. "We were about done ourselves. Only a little while ago—I can't remember the days now—we had to leave Scott and Hubbard when they gave out. We didn't even look back when we walked away from them."

Angry and disgusted, Godey walked away from Haler and stood looking upriver until his temper cooled. After a while he set out again, taking Haler with him and leaving the two Indians to help the men in camp.

They found Scott alive. Hubbard was dead in the

snow. Godey sent Scott and Haler back to the camp be-
low. Continuing the search with the Mexican packers,
Godey found Josiah Ferguson alive, and then Benjamin
Beadle—dead.

One by one he was accounting for all members of the
expedition.

"How far to where you last saw the Kerns?" Godey
asked Ferguson.

"They're ahead somewhere, the three Kerns, Captain
Cathcart and some others."

"Downriver? You're sure of that?"

Ferguson was positive of the fact.

Godey faced a hard decision. In his hurry, after seeing
the desperate condition of some of the survivors, he had
taken a shortcut across a loop of the river. It was possible
that the Kern party was somewhere along that bend, as
Ferguson contended. But if they were not there, Godey
would lose a day searching in the wrong place.

A day, even an hour, might mean the difference between life and death for some of the survivors. If he disre-
garded Ferguson's statement—the man was nearly blind
and in no condition to know where anyone was—and went
upriver, it could be a worse mistake.

Godey decided to go downriver.

At a camp near a mudflat of the Rio Grande, only
Charles Taplin was able to stay on his feet for any period
of time. Looking like hairy skeletons, the others—helpless
and waiting—lay around the cottonwood fires.

Doc Kern had been in a coma for almost twenty-four

hours, but he had rallied and was sitting up. He wondered if he could muster strength to make the trip to the river, fifty feet away. Two days before he had scooped up water skippers, long-legged insects, from a pool. He had caught twenty-one of them in his hat, three for each man in the group.

Twenty-one bugs fairly divided. Sharing, Doc Kern thought, was the difference between this group and all the others. Whatever they had found—a scrawny hawk dead in the snow, a lean rabbit, a wolf carcass—they had shared equally.

They were near death now, but Doc Kern was not afraid. They had been men. Swearing to stick together, they had done so. They had left no man behind to face his last moments beside a lonely, dying fire.

Though young Andrews and Henry Rohrer had not been members of the Kern group, they had joined it when they no longer could keep up with Haler's party. The Kerns had taken them in, shared with them, and cared for them until they died.

Charles Taplin was twenty-nine, a veteran of two previous expeditions with Colonel Frémont. He sat on a log and tried to figure their chances of living. They were not good. He was the only man in the group who could travel. For almost a week they had been in this same camp.

He had never seen game so scarce. Along toward evening he would go out to try again. His face was sunken, his eyes enormous above his matted beard. It was an effort to lift his rifle and lay it across his bony legs to check the priming.

Lying on his side, Captain Cathcart chewed on a scrap of blanket. The taste was terrible and he had difficulty forcing the shreds of wool down. Miserable situation, he thought calmly. His wasted face seemed to be all nose and eyes as he studied Taplin.

Quite a chap, that Taplin. He could have gone on with the stronger group, the cowardly group, but he had chosen to stay and help those in desperate need. Except for Taplin's tireless efforts in securing a bit of game now and then, and his encouragement, this party would have been wrecked, Cathcart thought.

Well, it was wrecked anyway, but they had made a valiant try; and Taplin, among them all, was certainly a hero. I ought to tell him that, Cathcart thought, but Taplin wouldn't believe it about himself.

McGehee staggered to his feet and dragged a piece of wood to the fire. He sat down exhausted. All he could think of was something to eat, and if he didn't stop thinking about it, he felt that he would go out of his mind.

He reached down and tapped Stepperfeldt. "Think they'll find us before long, Step?"

Stepperfeldt grunted.

Ned and Dick Kern pulled themselves up and sat with their backs against a log. Ned's dark whiskers were a wild riot of growth under his thrusting cheekbones and staring eyes. "Maybe we can find some more dried rosebuds along the bank," he said.

"Don't waste your strength," Taplin said. "I may be able to get a deer this evening." He spoke with such confidence that everyone looked at him trustingly.

"You really think so?" McGehee asked wistfully.

"I'm going to try," Taplin answered. "We're not licked yet, not by any means. We'll help ourselves all we can, but don't forget that Colonel Frémont and Godey will be coming back as soon as they can."

Everyone brightened a little. Even Stepperfeldt struggled to a sitting position and looked downriver, as if he expected to see relief in sight.

For a while Taplin's encouragement was strengthening, but the men's minds were dulled by starvation, and despair was ever close.

Suddenly Stepperfeldt shouted, "They won't come! They're all like Haler!" He pounded the ground with a bony fist and began to sob.

That was enough to dispirit the entire party. Once more Taplin tried to rouse them from despair, but without success.

A cold wind from the mountains ran through the leafless cottonwoods. It blew choking smoke from the fire into haggard faces.

Across the river and somewhere out above the snowy plain, ravens were circling. Taplin watched them, trying to estimate the distance. There could be a dead wolf out there, or some other carcass that would provide a meal.

Taplin knew that his failing eyes had been playing him tricks lately. He could not be sure how many miles away the ravens were, and he knew it would be folly to waste too much strength for a scrap of meat that might be gone before he could reach it.

Still, if he could shoot one or two ravens and bring

back even the bones of whatever they were circling over, it would help a little.

Suddenly he stared across the river with an expression of disbelief. He thought he was seeing a horse and rider. He scrambled up for a better view.

It *was* a horse and rider! Taplin began to shout.

Apathetic men raised their heads to look at him dully.

"What's the matter?" McGehee asked.

"There's a rider!" Taplin shouted, pointing.

No one believed him, until Cathcart lurched to his feet and said, "I think it's Godey."

It *was* Alexis Godey, scouting a short distance ahead of the mules and horses that carried food. Men who had thought they had no strength left now danced around embracing each other, shouting.

Later, Godey got the true story of Haler's cowardly behavior from the Kern party. There had been no fair division of food. Though someone had killed a deer, the weaker men, struggling desperately to stay with the main body, had been given only a shoulder blade of the animal.

"We tried to get Haler to hold the whole group together," Ned Kern said bitterly. "He wouldn't do it."

"He finally said he no longer had any authority," McGehee said. "He declared that it was every man for himself, and then he took the strongest men and ran away from us. We kept in sight for a while, and then we were done."

Taplin had little to say, but his quietness confirmed everything the others said. Taplin was the man who should have been left in charge of the expedition, Godey thought, but he had fallen into disfavor with Frémont by arguing about the baggage when the expedition first began the disastrous retreat.

Thoughts of what should have been done were of no use now. Godey left food, some of the horses, and all but one of the packers with the Kern party. He and one packer went on up the river to save anyone who was left.

He still hoped to find Antoine and Tabeau alive. They were experienced men. They had suffered many hardships before, and they knew how to survive. It was possible that they had dug in somewhere and found enough game to keep from starving.

Godey did find them. Snow was drifting over Tabeau where he lay beside the ashes of a fire. Sitting against a log nearby was Antoine, who had turned back to stay beside a dying friend.

Alexis Godey looked briefly at the frozen bodies. He knelt in the snow with bowed head, and then he rose quickly and went on with the Mexican muleteer.

In a brush hut, where his friends had left him, Manuel was still alive. His feet were starting to heal and he was in good health. For nearly two weeks he had lived on mice, catching them with his hands when they came into the hut from their warm runways under the snow, and he had shot a few camp robber birds.

The muleteer, who had seen the wrecks of men all the way up the river, explained it simply, "Little moving. Big heart." He meant that Manuel had not overexerted himself and had held to courage.

"Carver." Manuel pointed toward the mountains.

He touched his finger to his temple and shook his head. He explained that John Carver had come by the brush hut one day, carrying a piece of deer meat. Carver said that he had to get back to the mountains to recover something he had left behind.

Supplying Manuel with food and extra blankets, Godey continued on up the little stream by which the broken expedition had retreated from the San Juans.

He found no sign of Carver.

Godey and the muleteer were now in deep snow, passing the desolate camps made weeks before. Some of the mules weakened and froze to death. Their loss forced Godey to turn back without the more valuable baggage he had intended to recover, but he did bring back some of Frémont's personal gear.

Gathering up Manuel and the other survivors as he came to them, Godey went back down the Rio Grande.

Preuss, Creutzfeldt and Ted were the only members of the expedition left in the little pueblo, for all the others had gone on to Taos. Inaction made Preuss fume. He could not speak Spanish, and had little desire to learn. Ted was restless, worried about Godey and the men still left along the Rio Grande.

And then, on February 6th, not waiting for Godey to pick them up, Haler, Ducatel, Scott, Martin, and Bacon arrived at the village.

Haler's first question was, "Where's Colonel Frémont?"

Apparently he had much to report, and wanted to do

his talking before anyone else from upriver reached Frémont. Haler's group gave the toll of known dead.

That was bad enough, but there were still men unac-
counted for. No one would know for certain about them
until Godey returned.

Haler's group went on to Taos.

As the days ran on into the third week of Godey's ab
sence, Ted grew more worried. He could see great storms
darkening the northern sky.

One day, helping a Mexican grind meal, he heard a
shout from the trail upriver. The whole pueblo turned out
to look.

Godey was coming in with the rest of the survivors.

Ted ran toward them, with Preuss at his heels. There
was Manuel, whom everyone had thought dead. Preuss
laughed and cried at the same time as he greeted Captain
Cathcart and Stepperfeldt.

After he had searched the faces of the survivors looking for Antoine and Tabeau, Ted walked beside Godey's
stirrup, reluctant to ask about them.

Godey sensed his thoughts. "They were together until
the end."

Ted felt tears start in his eyes.

"I too cried," Godey said.

The toll was ten men, almost a third of the expedition. Except for Godey, it would have been twice as high.

Two days later all the survivors were together in Taos.
Colonel Frémont had already made arrangements for
equipment and supplies to go on to California by a southern route.

So quickly did Frémont carry out his plans to resume the journey that Ted had no time to mourn about the failure in the San Juans.

On February 13, 1849, two days after the last survivors reached Taos, the expedition was moving again. Ted rode beside Godey. A warm wind was coming from the south. The snows of the San Juans were far behind them, and though Ted would never forget the harrowing experiences in the mountains, his mind was already reaching out eagerly toward the strange and wondrous things Godey had told him of the deserts far to the south.

And Afterward

NED, DICK, AND DOC KERN, Taplin, Old Bill, Captain Cathcart and Stepperfeldt did not go on to California with Frémont. Early in March of 1849, Old Bill and Doc Kern led a mule train up the Rio Grande to recover some of the expedition's baggage. Both were killed, either by their Mexican packers or by Indians.

Frémont went on to California without incident, by way of the Gila River Route and the Old Spanish Trail. A year and a half later he was a millionaire as a result of gold discoveries on land he owned on Mariposa Creek. He became one of the first two United States Senators from California.

In 1856, his strong opposition to slavery led to his nomination on the Republican ticket for president of the United States. He was defeated by James Buchanan. Soon after the start of the Civil War, he was appointed a major general in the Union forces.

Again he was nominated for president, in 1864, this time by radical Republicans, but he withdrew when he realized his running would split the Republican vote and result in the defeat of Abraham Lincoln.

He died in New York in 1890.

It is for his explorations that he is best remembered today. Rivers, towns, counties, and mountains of the West bear his name.

Neither he nor Senator Benton ever admitted that the fourth expedition had failed. They both declared that Frémont had discovered what he set out to find; though when Frémont later backed a railroad with his own fortune—and lost it—the proposed route was a southern one, not through the San Juans.

In 1853, Frémont led a fifth expedition, crossing Cochetopa Pass some twenty miles north of Camp Desolation. It was a mild winter and he had no mishaps in Colorado, but he encountered big snow troubles later in the mountains of Utah and barely got through.

Frémont blamed Old Bill Williams for leading him astray on the fourth expedition. Old Bill was dead, but others have defended him against Frémont's accusations. It is obvious that they both made serious errors: Old Bill in his selection of a pass, Frémont in his insistence on bucking the Colorado Rockies during a blizzard winter.

Starting from Kansas City, Missouri, the route of the fourth expedition lies close to Highway 10, crosses the Wakarusa River near Eudora, Kansas, follows the south side of the Kaw (or Kansas) River to Lawrence, winds over the wooded hills to the old Pottawattamie Mission near Topeka, thence westward to the vicinities of Manhattan, Junction City, Abilene, and Salina.

South of Hays the expedition veered toward the Arkansas River, striking it just east of Dodge City. From there, until Frémont turned into the Wet Mountains west of Pueblo, Colorado, the expedition was close to the Arkansas all the way.

Lamar, Colorado, now stands where the enormous grove of cottonwoods, known as Big Timbers, sheltered the Indians, where old Tom Fitzpatrick worked so hard as Indian agent.

The site of famous Bent's Fort is a few miles from Las Animas, Colorado. Though the great structure is gone, its foundations have been carefully restored by the Colorado State Historical Society.

El Pueblo (or Fort Pueblo) is recalled only by a model in the State Historical Museum at Pueblo, Colorado. The original fort stood in a bend of the Arkansas near the Sante Fe station on North Union Avenue.

State Highway 96 follows Frémont's trail into the Wet Mountain Valley. Our present Mosca Pass is Robidoux's old pass. The Great Sand Dunes National Monument where Frémont emerged from the Sangre de Cristos is about twenty miles, as the crow flies, northeast of Alamosa, Colorado, and can be reached today by excellent roads.

In crossing the San Luis Valley, the expedition camped near what is now Hooper. They reached the Rio

Grande near the site of Monte Vista, and went on up to
where the towns of Del Norte and South Fork now stand.

They plunged into the mountains on Alder Creek,
which flows into the Rio Grande from the north, close to
the town of South Fork.

Their terrible struggle upward through the snow
brought them to the top of what is now named the La
Garita Mountains. They crossed to the head of Wannamaker Creek, and there for five days they were pinned
down in Camp Desolation by furious storms that wrecked
their last hope of going on.

In retreat, they sought a better way than the Alder
Creek route. Camp Hope was near the head of Embargo
Creek. It is marked today by a Forest Service sign. Relics
of the expedition may still be found at the high camps of
the expedition.

They straggled down Embargo Creek to the Rio
Grande, about halfway between South Fork and Del
Norte.

The mouth of the Conejos River, near where Frémont's
relief party found the survivors of King's group, is about
fourteen miles south of Alamosa. By Frémont's route, it is
about fifty miles from the Conejos to the site of the little
village where the survivors found succor, near present
Questa, New Mexico.

Taos, town of ancient pueblos, marked the end of
the fourth expedition, no matter if Frémont did continue
with part of his men to California.

If storms had not stopped him at the head of Wannamaker Creek, he would have gone on. It is about five miles

down Wannamaker to the old mining camp of Sky City in Saguache Park. From there to the head of Mexican Joe Gulch, at a low divide between East and West, it is ten miles, with no hard climbing involved.

From there—well, it would be second-guessing history even to speculate on how far Frémont could have gone.

About the Author

.

STEVE FRAZEE is a native of Colorado and a graduate of its Western State College. He has worked as newspaperman, miner, construction superintendent, and is a successful writer of novels. He is the author of *First through the Grand Canyon*: The Expedition of Major John Wesley Powell.

Mr. Frazee is an expert white water man and mountain climber; these skills greatly aided his research on both the expeditions of Major Powell and Colonel Frémont. Before writing *Year of the Big Snow*, he climbed the Sangre de Cristo Mountains, following as closely as possible the route Frémont took. The area of Frémont's bitterest struggles and eventual defeat lies close to Mr. Frazee's home in Colorado. He has visited the Fourth Expedition's campsites, and in one place, he reports finding the bones of the mules still lying on the mountainside.